Technology of Skilled Processes

Basic Engineering Competences

Assembling and Dismantling

Editorial Panel

M. Leaf, Grad I Plant Eng, T Eng

V. Green, TEng (CEI), MBIM
Head of Department of Engineering Crafts
Huddersfield Technical College

C. Sutcliffe, OBE, MSc, C Eng, MIMechE
Vocational Curriculum Services
City and Guilds of London Institute

Published as a co-operative venture between
Stam Press Ltd
and

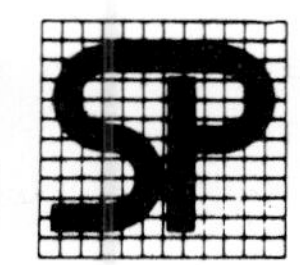

City and Guilds

Syllabus

Technology of Skilled Processes 367-1

Section	Process
1	Observing Safe Practices
2	Moving Loads
3	Measurement and Dimensional Control (1)
4	Marking Out
5	Work and Toolholding
6	Removing Material
7	Forming
8	Joining
9	Fabrication
10	Soft Soldering, Hard Soldering and Brazing
11	Fusion Welding
12	Power Transmission
13	Assembly and Dismantling (1)
14	Interpreting Drawings, Specifications and Data

Syllabus

Basic Engineering Competences 201

Basic Engineering Technology
201-1-01

01 Industrial Studies
02 Observing Safe Practices
03 Moving Loads
04 Measurement and Dimensional Control (1)
05 Marking Out
06 Work and Toolholding
07 Removing Material
08 Joining
09 Interpreting Drawings, Specifications and Data
010 Assembly and Dismantling (1)

Basic Fabrication and Welding Technology
201-1-07

01 Forming
02 Fabrication
03 Soft Soldering, Hard Soldering and Brazing
04 Fusion Welding

Basic Maintenance Technology
201-1-09

01 Forming
02 Soft Soldering, Hard Soldering and Brazing
03 Power Transmission
04 Measurement and Testing of Electro-Mechanical Systems (1)

Science Background to Technology
201-1-04

01 Basic Physical Quantities, Electricity and Magnetism
02 Forces
03 Pressure
04 The Principles of Tool Construction; Materials Technology

SUPPORTING BOOKS

Book titles	Covering	Covering
Basic Engineering	**Syllabus** 367-1	Syllabus 201-1-01
Observing Safe Practices and Moving Loads	Section 1 and 2	02-03
Measuring and Marking Out	Section 3 and 4	04-05
Workholding and Toolholding, Removing Material	Section 5 and 6	06-07
Joining	Section 8	08
Interpreting Drawings, Specifications and Data	Section 14	09
Assembling and Dismantling	Section 13	10
Fabrication and Welding		Syllabus 201-1-07
Forming	Section 7	01
Fabrication	Section 9	02
Soft Soldering, Hard Soldering and Brazing	Section 10	03
Fusion Welding	Section 11	04
Maintenance		Syllabus 201-1-09
Forming	Section 7	01
Soft Soldering, Hard Soldering and Brazing	Section 10	02
Power Transmission	Section 12	03
Science		Syllabus 201-1-04
Basic Physical Quantities, Electricity and Magnetism		01
Forces		02
Pressure		03
Principles of Tool Construction: Materials Technology		04

201 – Basic Engineering Competences
201-1-01 Basic Engineering Technology

The contents of this book have been designed to cover the requirements of the City and Guilds Basic Competence Syllabus (367-1), section 13. The contents of component 10 of the City and Guilds Basic Engineering Technology Syllabus 201-1-01 are identical, except for minor points, and are equally covered by this book.

As listed, the heading references in this book conform with those in the syllabus section 13 of scheme 367-1. In the 201 scheme syllabus items are numbered sequentially and prefixed with the component number, e.g. item 1 in syllabus 04 is 4.1.
Below, in brackets following the page numbers, we give the 201 syllabus sequence numbers.

Contents Assembling and Dismantling

(continued)

SAFETY

The subject of safety generally is covered in the series book *Observing Safe Practices and Moving Loads*. Students doing practical work relating to the matter in this book are expected to have completed the safety syllabus. It must be understood that all operations involving moving machinery are hazardous. It is therefore essential that all tasks are performed to a safe system of work with adequate supervision and that all safety rules are followed.

First published in Great Britain 1987
as a co-operative venture between Stam Press Ltd and the City and Guilds of London Institute

Reprinted 1988

ISBN 0 85973 0239

Printed and bound in Great Britain by Martin's of Berwick

This book is intended for those who are, or will be, doing a practical job in industry.
It is specially written for those who need their technology as a background to their work and as a means of adapting to changes in working practices caused by technological advance. Where words such as "he" or "craftsman" appear in this series, they are to be interpreted as "he/she", "craftsman/woman".
This new series of textbooks presents the technology in terms of competence rather than working from a conventional theoretical base, i.e. the material will help readers understand:

- the use of
- the change to
- the development of
- other uses of

industrial process technology and skills.

This book has been compiled after a survey of the industrial skilled processes which form the nucleus of occupational schemes and pre-vocational courses of the City and Guilds of London Institute and a comparison with provisions elsewhere in Europe.

Three basic facts emerged:

- the technology is common to many different schemes though the contexts of applications are very different;
- the technology is being taught in a variety of workshops in a variety of exercises related to the immediate needs of students and their industries; these industrially-related exercises formed excellent learning tasks and provided clear motivation for students because of their immediate relevance;
- the technology is so well integrated with the 'first-task need' that students did not recognise its relevance to many other tasks they would be called upon to perform.

This book seeks to build on the learning tasks and to provide a means of learning and generalising the technology, so that the immediate job is better understood and better done, new tasks using the same process technology are more quickly mastered and updating or retraining is easier and more effective.
The editors would welcome further constructive suggestions which should be addressed to:
Stam Press Ltd
Old Station Drive
Leckhampton
Cheltenham GL53 0DN

Technology of Skilled Processes

Project Structure and Use of Syllabus Bank and Supporting Books

1 The TECHNOLOGY associated with a given industrial process is a common requirement, but the APPLICATIONS vary by occupation and task, so a distinction has to be made between:

(a) THE AIM of the process: eg. to bend, metals, to drill, etc.

(b) THE LEARNING and ASSESSMENT: related to the application(s) specific to the industry to which the candidate belongs or aspires, or to the context of scheme chosen as a basis of study.

2 The approach suggested for the learning and assessment of any process technology is as follows:

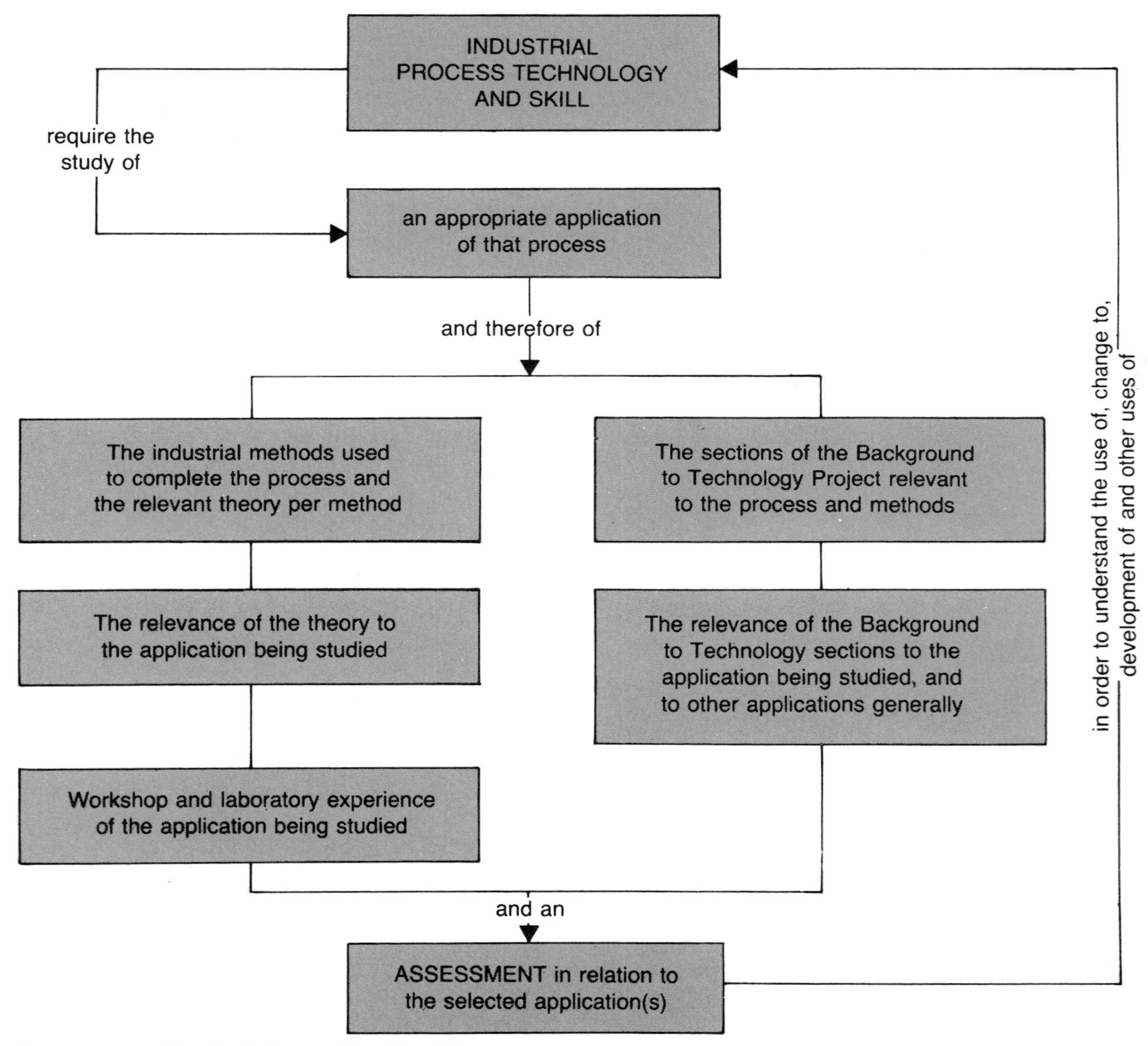

1 Introduction to assembling and dismantling

As every technical product consisting of a number of components must be assembled before it can be dismantled, we shall, throughout this book, consistently follow the sequence:

- Assembling
- Dismantling.

This book is intended to provide the student with a fundamental knowledge of assembling and dismantling in order to help acquire skills needed at a basic level. In addition he should be able to select the correct methods and sequences, to apply the appropriate tools to the task and should also gain an initial understanding of component construction, materials and tool construction.

The text has been written with these aims in mind and it is designed to form a basis from which the student can move on to a more advanced level.

Correct assembling and dismantling require knowledge and experience. Experience is not something that you can learn from books, though books can emphasise the value of certain points and techniques learned. Practice, however, is necessary to extend experience and knowledge, and will lead to more efficient assembling and dismantling. Structured practical training is a safe and efficient way of providing knowledge and real (or simulated) experience in these processes.

It is important here to mention safety. In the course of assembling and dismantling, safe practice must be learned and observed from the outset. General safety matters are discussed in the series book *Observing Safe Practices and Moving Loads*. In this present volume we shall mention specific safety aspects of particular importance when they are relevant. For your own safety and that of others make sure that you always know and follow the appropriate safety rules.

1.a The purpose of assembling

The purpose of assembling is to put separate parts together to form a whole component, structure or system.
During the assembling process, regard must be paid to the following points:

1.a.i Sequence of assembly

The correct sequence of assembly operations must be followed. In Fig. **1**.1 the key (1) must be inserted before the pulley (2) is driven on to the shaft. The screw (3) must be tightened after the pulley is positioned correctly.

1.a.ii Technique of joining

A fitting method must be planned in advance. There could be alternative methods for assembling the bearings shown in Fig. **1**.2. They could be heated in oil and then assembled in position on the shaft. Alternatively, they could be forced on to the shaft using a press or a hammer. Whatever method is chosen should be planned in advance and carried out with care.

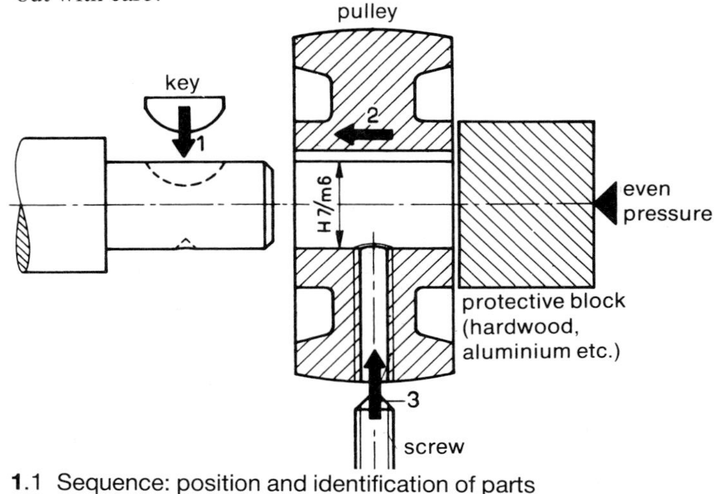

1.1 Sequence: position and identification of parts

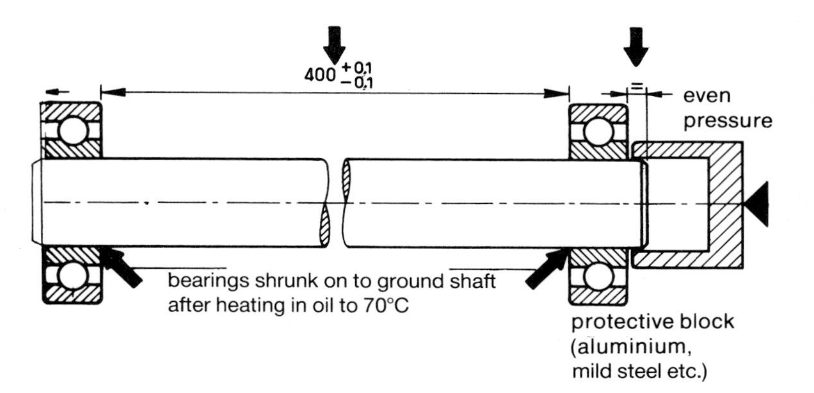

1.2 Method of fitting and placing

1.a.iii Position of joints

Parts must be fitted in a place determined in advance. Fig. **1**.2 shows the bearings placed at the same distance from their respective shaft ends.

1.a.iv Inter-relationship and identification of parts

Identification of parts and their position is usually found by referring to the assembly drawing. Fig. **1**.3 shows the position of the holes relative to the axis. For further examples of engineering drawings you should refer to the Appendix.

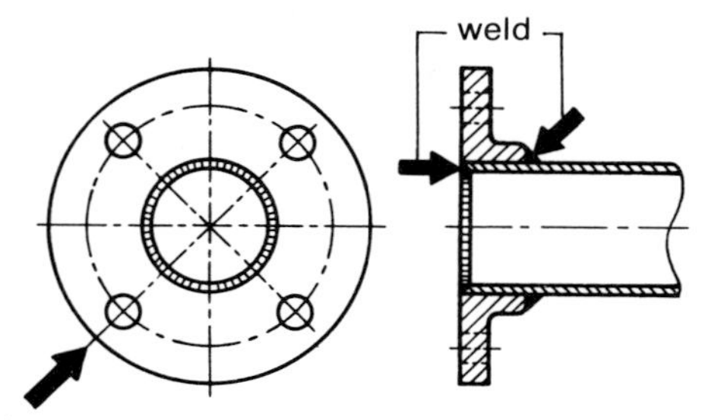

1.3 Method of fitting and placing

1.a.v Tolerances

Assembly components must be fitted together with fits determined in advance. Light pressure applied to the pulley shown in Fig. **1**.1 enables it to be assembled with the correct fit on the shaft. The fit is indicated in the drawing by the combination of letters and numbers shown. British Standard (BS) 4500 lists the fits and recommended tolerances, while the series books *Joining, Fabrication* and *Interpreting Drawings, Specifications and Data* provide additional information relevant to the assembly of components.

1.a.vi Protection of parts against damage and/or corrosion

Parts must be protected against damage and corrosion. In Figs. **1**.1 and **1**.2 the use of soft materials to protect the pulley and bearings against pressure or impact is illustrated. In Fig. **1**.4a a protective coating is used after the zinc has been removed by screw-cutting, so that after assembly the pipe will not corrode. In Figs. **1**.4b and **1**.4c parts are shown protected by coverings such as oil, greaseproof paper and plastic caps, to ensure that when assembled they are free of contaminants and do not carry any harmful particles that might cause premature wear of or failure the assembly.

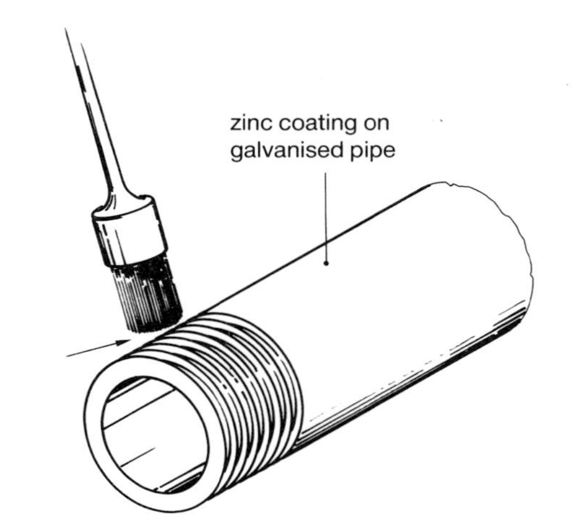

a Applying a protective coating to a freshly machined screw thread

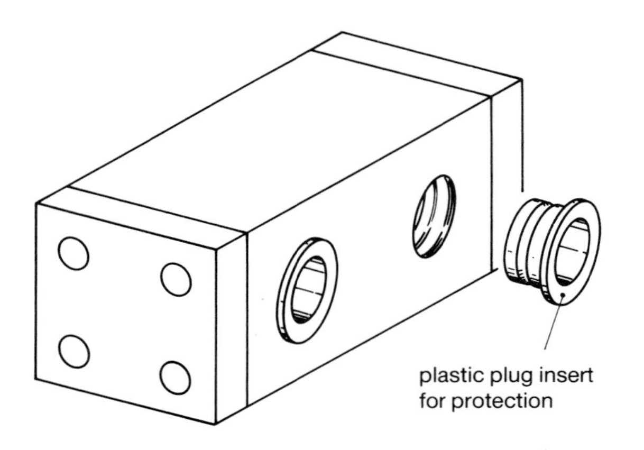

b Use of plastic inserts to prevent entry of contaminants

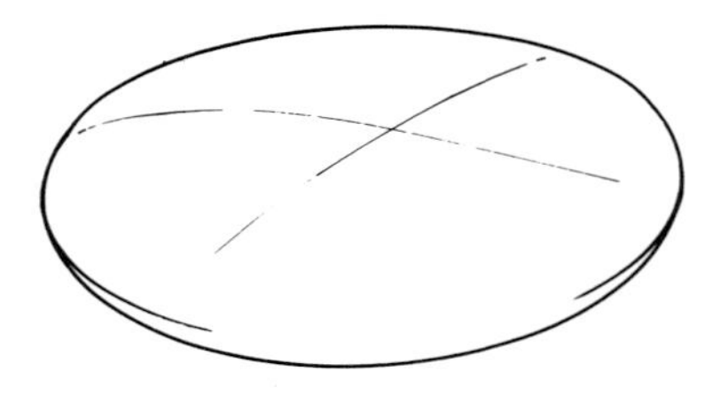

c Plastic or greaseproof paper cover used to wrap components

1.4 Protection of parts

1.a.vii Specifications and standards

The assembly may need to conform to standards laid down in advance, i.e. bolts to BS 3692, limits and fits to BS 4500 and drawings to BS 308.

1.a.viii Design considerations

Most assemblies must be able to be dismantled. Reasons for this will be explained next, but it should be noted that some assemblies are designed to last a useful life without servicing and then be replaced by an identical unit. Examples of these are car water pumps and domestic refrigerator units.

1.b The purpose of dismantling

Dismantling is the act of taking apart, completely or partially, a machine or mechanism, tool or other construction for one or more of the following reasons:

1.b.i Periodic inspection and maintenance

Periodic inspection to check operation, examine for wear and, if necessary, the cleaning of parts. In Fig. **1**.5 the covers have been dismantled so that the transmission parts can be inspected for wear and to enable cleaning to be carried out.

1.5 Inspection and cleaning

1.b.ii Repair of components

Even when a part may be repairable without removal, it is hardly ever possible to gain adequate access without some dismantling of the assembly.

1.b.iii Replacement of worn components

The comments under **1**.b.ii on gaining access also apply when a part is to be replaced rather than repaired.

1.b.iv Transport of systems for later re-assembly on site

Fig. **1**.6 shows a crane being transported in sections. Without dismantling it may be impracticable or prohibitively expensive to move the crane.

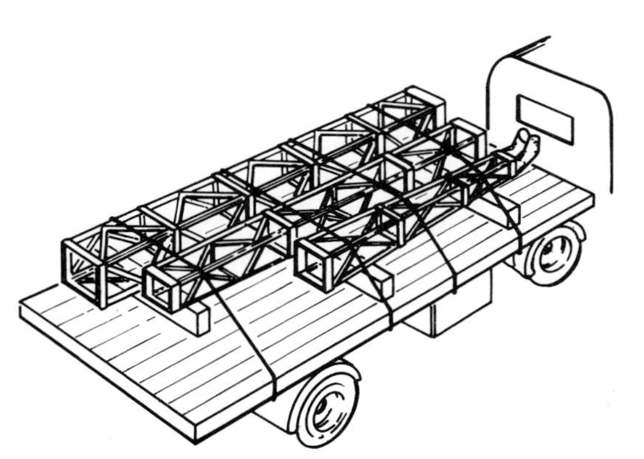

1.6 Transport

2 Methods of assembling and dismantling

2.a Methods of assembling

The difference between the following methods of assembling can be seen by observing in each case how they are carried out:

- By partial fabrication, fitting and assembling on the site
- 'One off' assembly, i.e. assembling single objects on the workbench
- 'Batch assembly', i.e. assembling a series of identical objects
- Assembling on site without prefabrication
- Assembling on an assembly line
- Assembling of large structures
- Assembling of trial erections.

2.a.i Partial fabrication followed by on-site assembly and fitting

An example of this method of operation is that followed by mechanics in constructing a central heating system. The pipes are cut to size, bent, assembled and fitted to other pipes or components in situ. The prepared and additional parts (radiators, valves) are 'laced' together on site. The method is illustrated in Fig. **2.1**, the working sequence being indicated by numbers.

2.a.ii 'One off' assembly

In assembling a gear pump, all the parts are ready-made and the only work needed is correct fitting together, checking the operation, and making any necessary adjustments (Fig.**2.2**).

2.a.iii 'Batch' assembly

Fig. **2.3** shows a sequence of work where a series of identical gear pumps is assembled. The 'hatching' on the figure indicates the particular item/s assembled during a particular stage in the batch assembly.

2.a.iv 'On site' assembly without prefabrication

The installation of a centrifugal pump is shown in Fig. **2.4** as an example. This includes aligning the coupling of the electric motor and the pump, and the connection of both suction and pressure pipes. Important points for consideration are:

- accurate alignment of pump to motor
- pipe flanges should be parallel so that stress is not created when they are bolted together.

2.a.v Assembly line work

Assembly line work is shown in Figs. **2.5** and **2.6**. Note that for this type of assembling the use of robots is increasing.

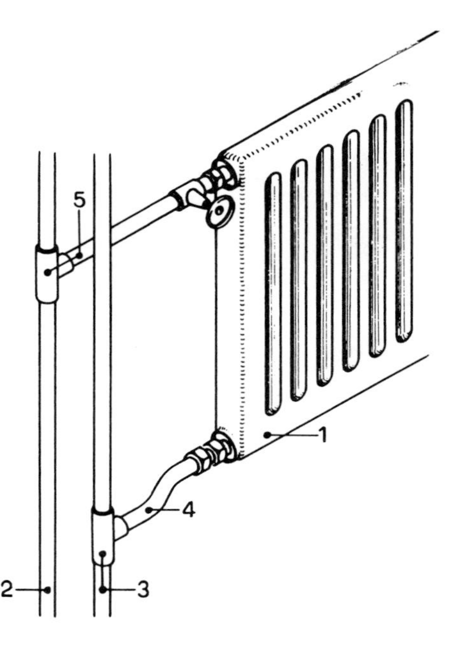

2.1 Fabrication, fitting and assembly on site

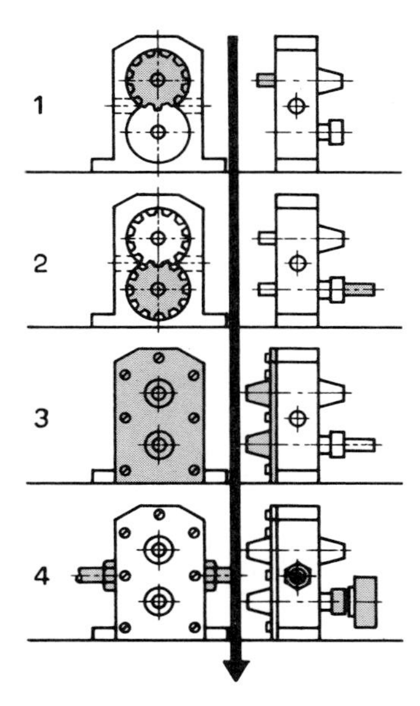

2.2 One-off assembly

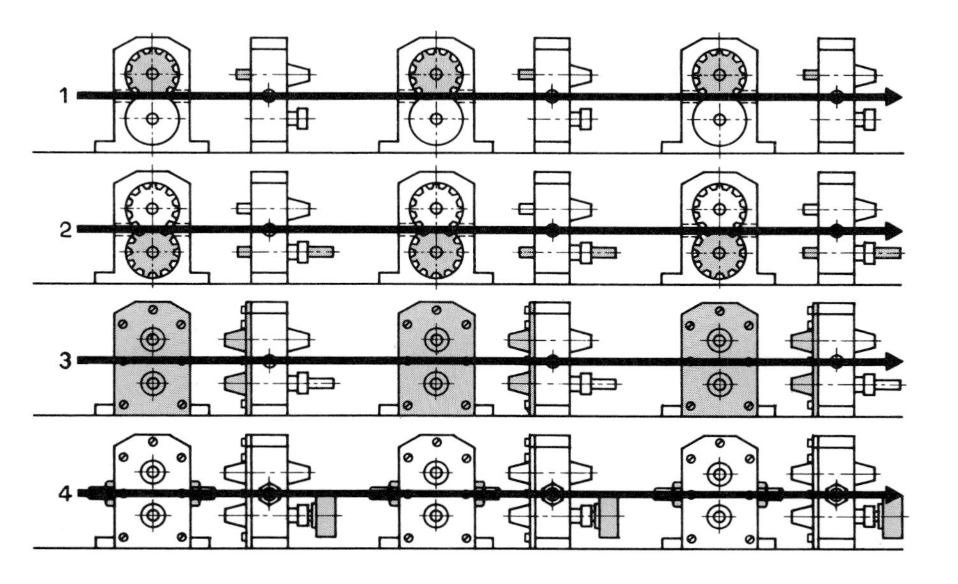

2.3 Batch assembly

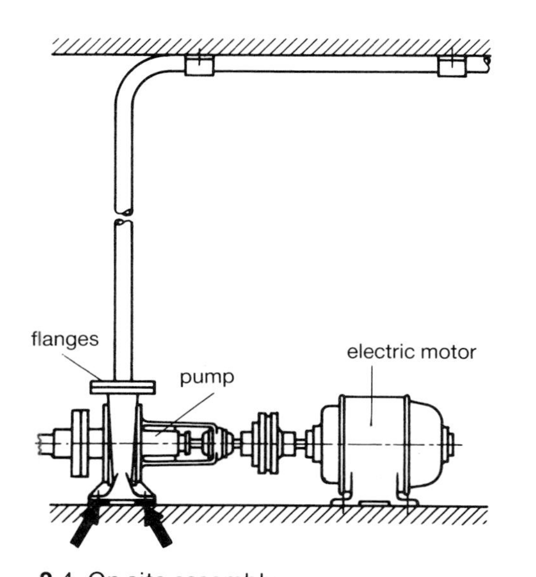

2.4 On site assembly

2.5 Assembly line work

2.6 Assembly line work

2.a.vi Large structure assembly

Good examples are the fitting out of ships and the construction of large chemical plants. Many assembly teams are at work at the same time, a factor that necessitates considerable pre-planning and consultation.

2.a.vii Trial erections

Examples in this category are large machines and fabrications such as rolling mills, cranes, etc. These are often erected on manufacturers' premises to test and modify the construction methods or working functions and to make it easier to mark parts/joints before dismantling and reassembling on site (Fig. **2**.7).

2.b Methods of dismantling

These procedures fall into three main categories:

- 'on site' dismantling and repair
- 'on site' dismantling prior to workshop repair
- 'on site' replacements of components and workshop reconditioning of replaced components.

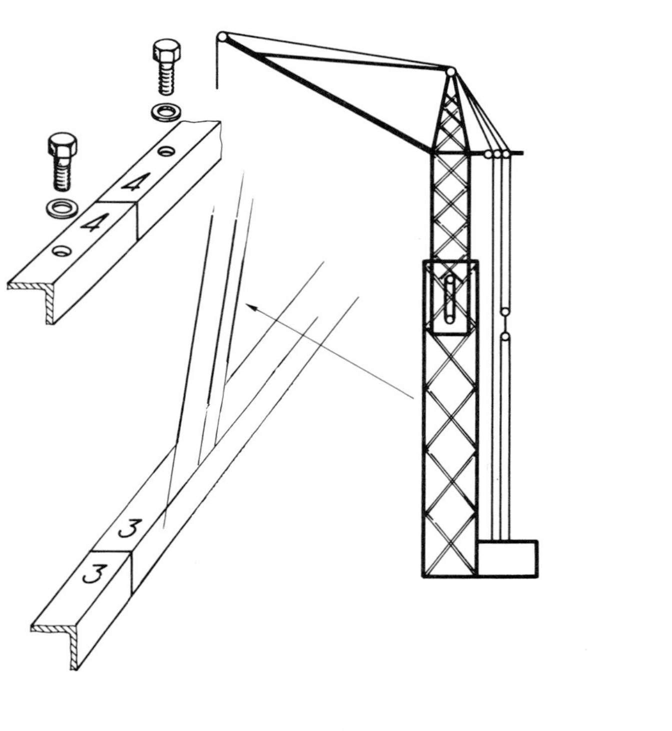

2.7 Trial erections, marking of parts

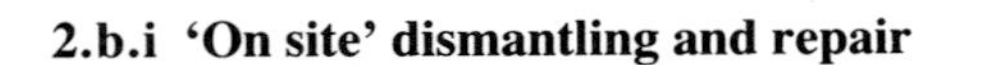

2.b.i 'On site' dismantling and repair

The example in Fig. **2**.8, shows a flexible coupling, where the rubber disc has to be replaced. This can be done on the site without any difficulty.

2.b.ii 'On site' dismantling before workshop repair

The pump shown in Fig. **2**.4 has to be dismantled from the motor and pipe lines because the bearings are worn. The pump bearings are replaced with new ones on the workbench and the pump is then assembled and reinstalled.

2.b.iii 'On site' replacement of components and workshop reconditioning of replaced components

The nozzle of the fuel pump of a diesel engine is shown in Fig. **2**.9. It is common practice to dismantle the nozzle assembly only, and replace it with a spare one. Afterwards the malfunctioning nozzle can be repaired in the user's workshop, or by a company specialising in this type of repair.

Note: Particular safety procedures must be observed when dismantling certain assemblies. See Section 8.

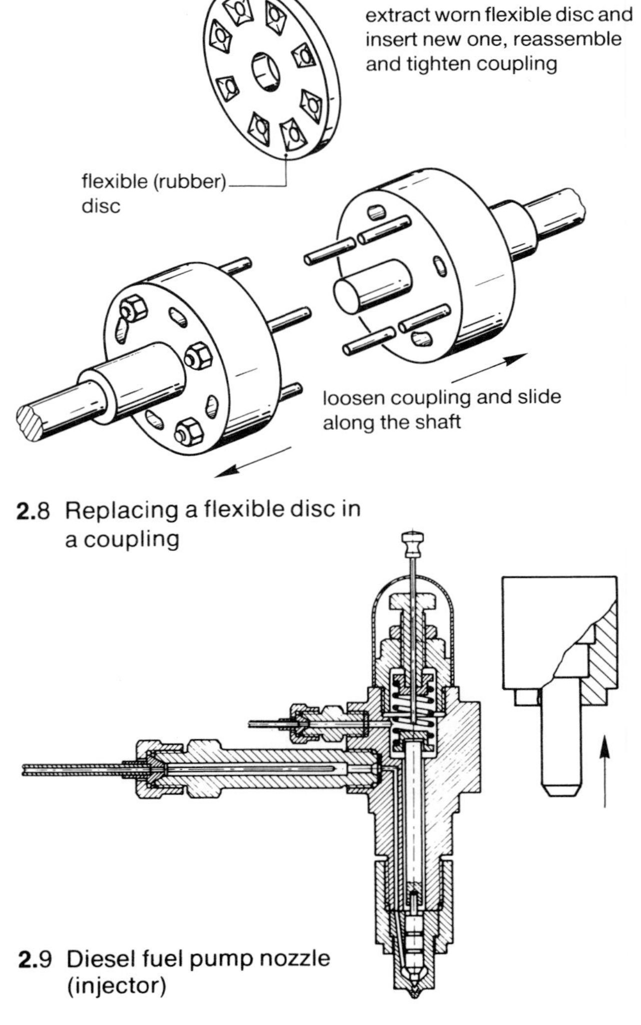

2.8 Replacing a flexible disc in a coupling

2.9 Diesel fuel pump nozzle (injector)

3 Selection of assembling and dismantling methods

3.a Selecting a method of assembling

The following points should be taken into account when selecting a method of assembling:

- sizes of systems and components
- presence of static and moving parts
- accuracy of tolerances required
- levels of accessibility required
- number of parts.

3.a.i Size and complexity of components and systems

Differences in size necessitate differences in technique. Fig. **3**.1a shows a 20 mm bearing being forced on to its seating by using a hammer and 'dolly', while a 200 mm bearing requires a much larger force and a press is being used (Fig. **3**.1b).

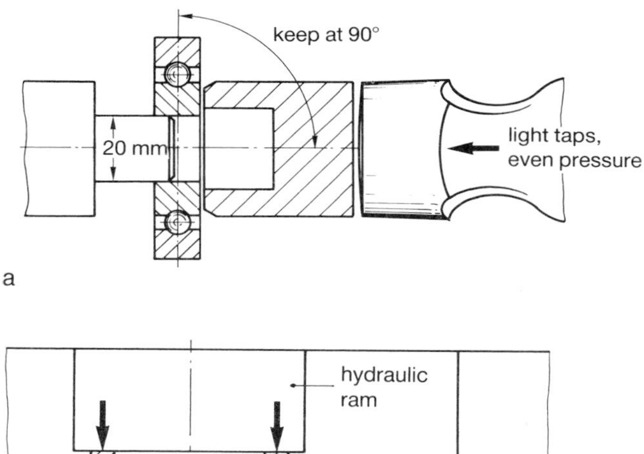

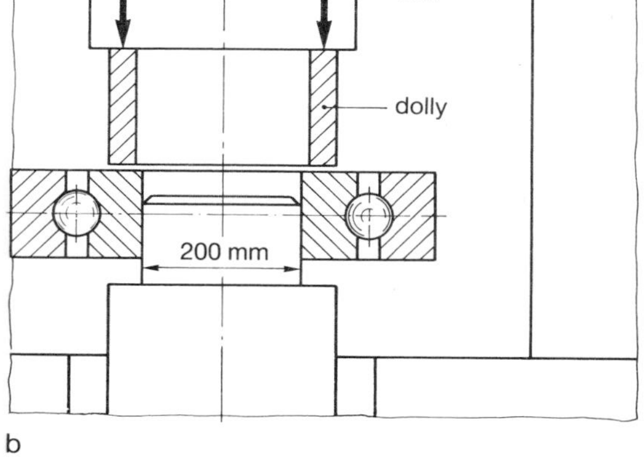

3.1 Fitting bearings

Fig. **3**.2 shows small assemblies (reduction gear boxes) being assembled on a workbench under clean conditions. Fig. **3**.3 on the other hand shows a large assembly of steelwork which will involve working at height, using lifting gear. Care must be taken with parts having large masses or size; suitable lifting gear and supports must be used. As such parts are moved into position you must ensure that neither your nor your companions are in danger of being trapped.

3.a.ii Static and moving parts

When considering movement one must distinguish between:

- *Objects that have nearly all static parts*. The structural steel assembly in Fig. **3**.3 has many static parts. It is important to get things right first time. For example if

3.2 Small assemblies on a workbench

3.3 Large assemblies (structural steelwork)

the holes are to be in correct alignment the girder must be positioned correctly. Later dismantling and redrilling will be avoided by first referring to drawings and plans.

- *Objects that have many moving parts*. Fig. **3**.4 shows a robot arm which has to move in all directions with very great accuracy. These movements are governed by numerous individual components, the assembly of which is highly critical. Careful checking of assembly sequence, position and place is very important when assembling complex components or those having many moving parts. This may prevent the need later for dismantling and refitting of parts. Once again, where assemblies have moving parts care must be taken to avoid trapping yourself or your companions during assembly.

3.a.iii Accuracy of tolerances required

The requirements for assembling a loosely toleranced component will not be as demanding as those for one which is closely toleranced. The trolley wheel (Fig. **3**.5) will simply slip on the axle and be secured by the split pin, but in the bearing assembly (Fig. **3**.6) care must be taken to align and 'bed-in' the bearing. Fitting the bearing requires considerable skill, whereas assembling the trolley wheel to the shaft requires very little.

3.a.iv Levels of accessibility required

Assembling can be very difficult when the part or job is in an awkward place and is difficult to reach (Fig. **3**.7).

3.4 An assembly with many moving parts

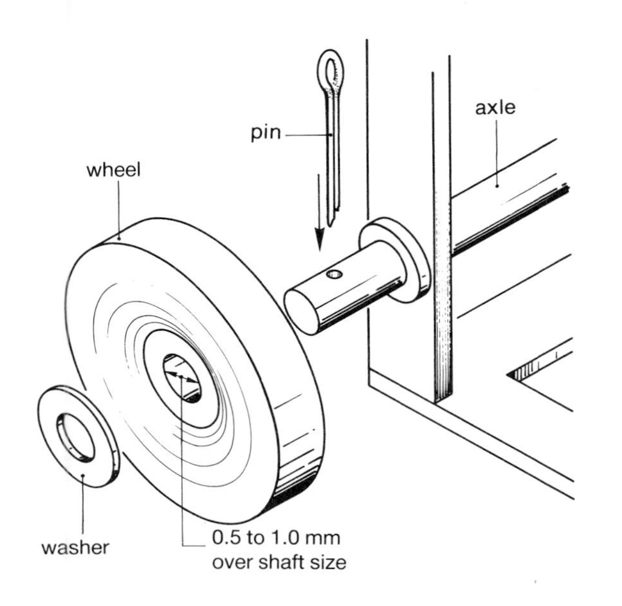

3.5 Assembling a loosely toleranced component

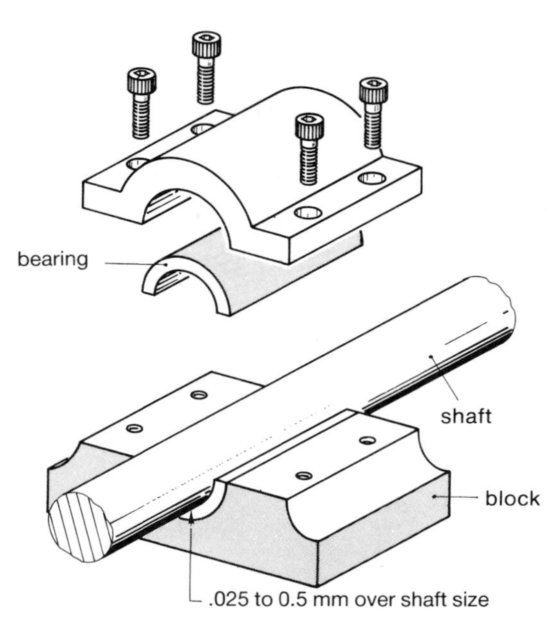

3.6 Assembling a closely toleranced component

Positioning a component is a design consideration, and there is often a conflict between efficiency in performing a function and ease of access for maintenance.

3.a.v Number of parts

As a general rule assemblies comprising many separate components present more problems than assemblies with few parts (Fig. **3.8**). These problems will be discussed later.

3.7 An assembly where access is difficult

3.b Selecting the method of dismantling

In the following examples of the dismantling process you will note several typical factors affecting the dismantling process and some important factors influencing how it is done.

3.b.i Form of transport available for the dismantled system

If we consider the dismantling of newly built constructions, a crane is a good example (Fig. **2.7**). It is carefully built and tested first, to ensure that it meets the required specification and safety standards. Consideration must be

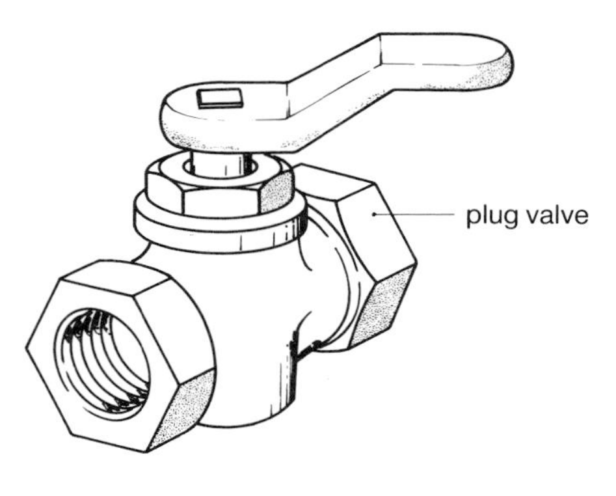

3.8 An object with few parts

3.9 A crankshaft

given to its method of transportation (Fig. **1**.6) in units which are as large as possible, to the site for re-erection. In addition to the method of transport, the size and weight of the units have to be considered in relation to the off-loading facilities at the site.

3.b.ii Nature of repairs to be undertaken

Fig. **3**.9 shows the removal of a crankshaft from its base. The engine needs to be dismantled so that the worn bearings can be replaced. A major consideration affecting the procedure will be whether replacement is to be carried out in situ or in a workshop. That choice is normally made by considering the practical and economic factors for and against each method.

3.b.iii The size of the system and components

Dismantling the engine and removing the crankshaft shown in Fig. **3**.9 needs methods and equipment on a totally different scale from dismantling the small electric drill shown in Fig. **3**.10. The latter can be stripped on any workshop bench. Among other complications, the crankshaft in Fig. **3**.9 requires the skilled operation of lifting gear with a capacity of several tonnes.

3.10 Exploded view of an electric drill

3.b.iv Accuracies of fit involved

Dismantling the trolley wheels shown in Fig. **3**.11 and Fig. **3**.5 will not require the same degree of care as dismantling the closely toleranced shaft and bearing of Fig. **3**.12 where neither bearing nor shaft must be damaged. The trolley wheel can be removed when the pin has been pulled from the hole by using pliers, protection of the parts being unnecessary. In the case of the shaft and bearing much skill is required to balance the shaft, and the parts must be protected from damage by using appropriate supports and packing. Unless great care is taken the relatively soft bearing may be scored or deformed by the shaft or lifting equipment.

3.b.v Later on-site assembly conditions

To re-assemble parts of a mechanism, special tools or presses may be needed. We must also make sure that there is adequate clearance for their application. Lifting gear may be required which, if headroom is restricted, may mean using jacks rather than a crane or overhead tackle.

3.11 Little accuracy needed

3.12 Great accuracy and care needed

3.b.vi Number of parts

Fig. **3.**13 shows a view of the parts of a lathe. Note that, as in many assemblies, there are a number of 'units' here (e.g. the loose-head). Normally, dismantling will be confined to the unit needing attention. Mating parts will be kept together and, if necessary, carefully marked to show precise relationship (Fig. **3.**14).

3.b.vii Ease or difficulty of dismantling given joints

Fig. **3.**15 shows a joint which after some time in service has become rusted. Applying penetrating oil and using a hydraulic drawer is one method of dismantling this joint.

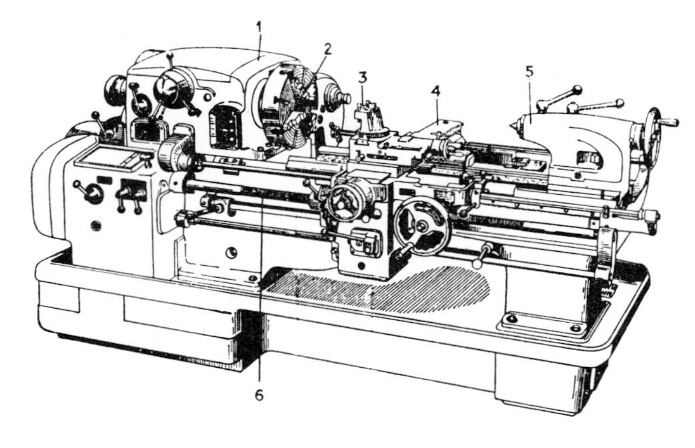

1 Headstock
2 Chuck
3 Tool post
4 Saddle
5 Tailstock (loose-head)
6 Screw

3.13 The parts of a lathe

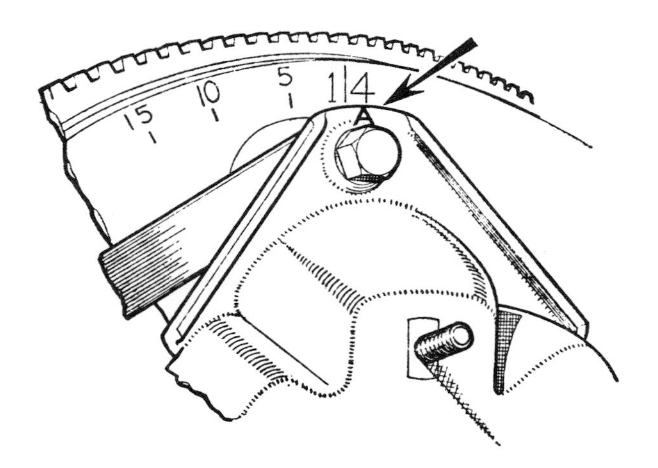

3.14 Marking of mating parts – clutch cover balance mark and flywheel timing mark on a motor vehicle

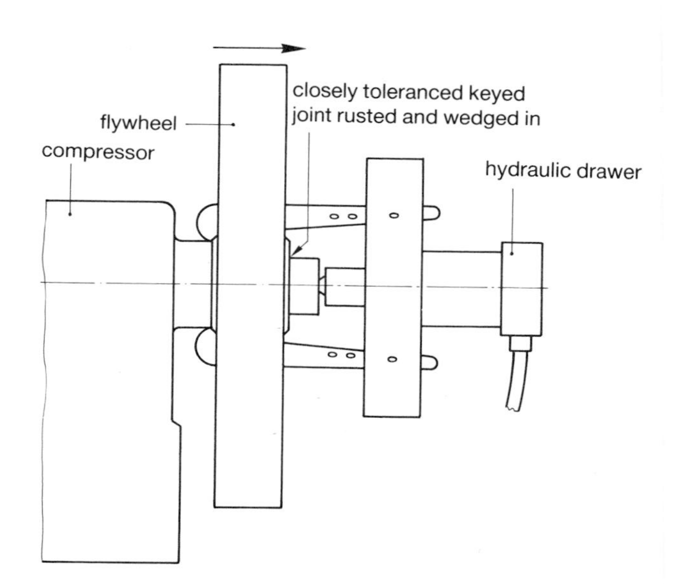

3.15 Pulling flywheel from shaft after applying penetrating fluid

4 Relationship between assembled components

The need to provide for relative movement, or positively exclude it, is an important consideration affecting the design of mating or adjoining parts of a mechanism. The need for fluid-tightness frequently occurs at the same time. The range of these relationships is demonstrated by the following.

4.a-f Typical examples of mating or adjoining components

- Neither component moves relative to the other. Fig. **4.**1 shows flanges of a coupling bolted so that they cannot move.
- The assembled parts do not move relative to each other and in addition the joint has to be fluid tight. Fig. **4.**2 shows a pipe flange joint with a packing ring.
- One of the assembled parts must be able to slide relative to the other. Fig. **4.**3 shows a simple shaft connector.
- One of the assembled parts must be able to slide but must also be fluid tight. Fig. **4.**4 shows a double acting hydraulic piston within a cylinder.
- One of the parts must be able to rotate relative to the other. Fig. **4.**5 shows a wheel and fixed axle.
- One of the assembled parts must rotate relative to the other, while at the same time the assembly must be fluid tight. Fig. **4.**6 shows the packing and stem of a valve assembly.

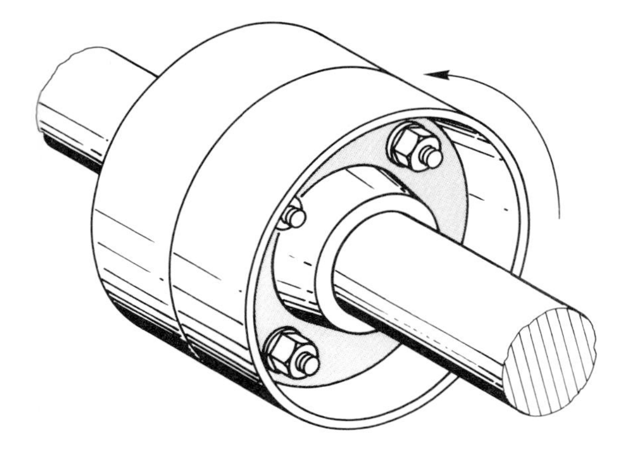

4.1 A coupling

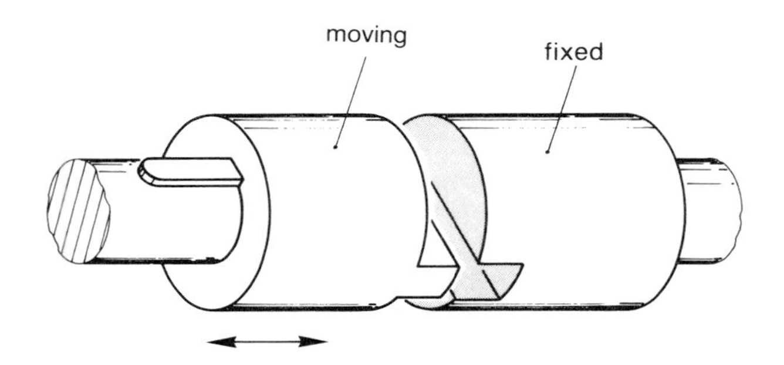

4.3 A shaft connector

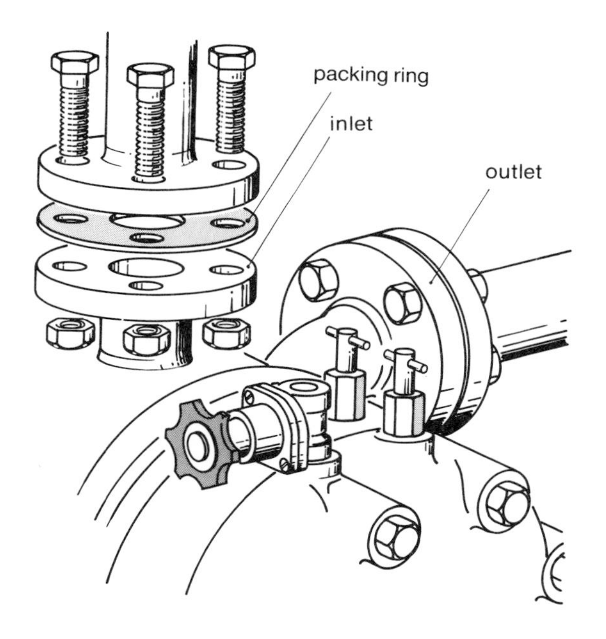

4.2 Flanges

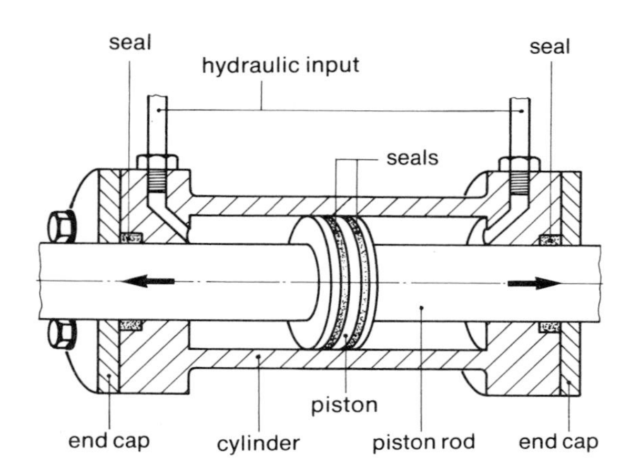

4.4 Double acting hydraulic piston within a cylinder

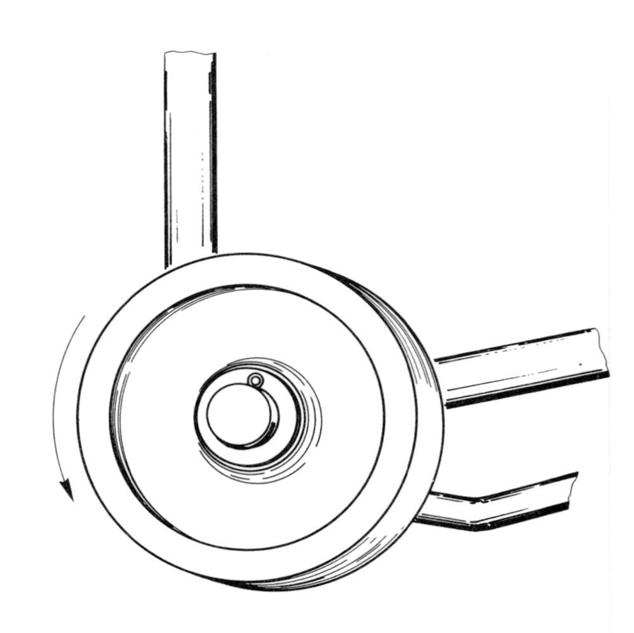

4.5 A wheel and fixed axle

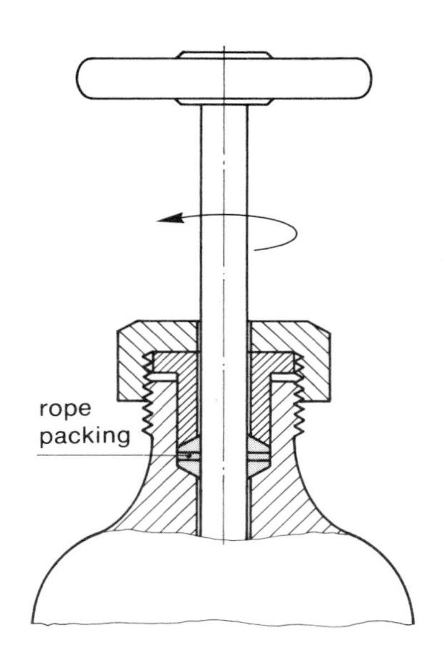

4.6 A rotating valve stem

5 Forces and their effects in assembling and dismantling

The application of the correct amount of force is of the utmost importance in assembling and dismantling. Whether lifting, moving, tightening or slackening off, great care must be taken if damage is to be avoided to persons or parts. Too much force can lead to damage of parts or even personal injury. Too little force will result in a loose assembly, causing damage.
Tensile, shear, compressive and bending forces may all be present in assemblies or during the assembling or dismantling processes. We shall confine discussion to the forces associated with bolts, nuts, pins and keys.

5.a Effect on bolts and nuts

All the forces or loads already mentioned, singly or in combination, can affect bolts and nuts. In addition the effect may vary between their parts, as will be seen from the following.

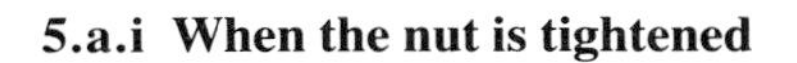

5.a.i When the nut is tightened

The following occurs:

- the bolt shank is subjected to a tensile load (Fig. **5**.1)
- the threads of the bolt and the nut have to withstand a shear load. The shorter the thickness of the nut, the greater the possibility of shearing (Fig. **5**.2)
- the head of the bolt is in shear. The shorter the length of the head, the greater the possibility of shearing (Fig. **5**.3)

5.a.ii Stress situations in service

While a bolt is in service these typical situations may arise:

- the bolt is subjected to a tensile load caused by pressure (Fig. **5**.4) or weight (Fig. **5**.5)
- the bolt is subjected to compressive loads (Fig. **5**.6)
- the bolt is subjected to tensile and shear loads. The flanges of the coupling in Fig. **5**.7 are pressed against each other by tightening the bolts. This constitutes a tensile load in the bolt. Since the power has to be transmitted by the shafts, each bolt is also shear loaded.
- the bolt is being subjected to a bending load as well as the shear and tensile loads (Fig. **5**.8).

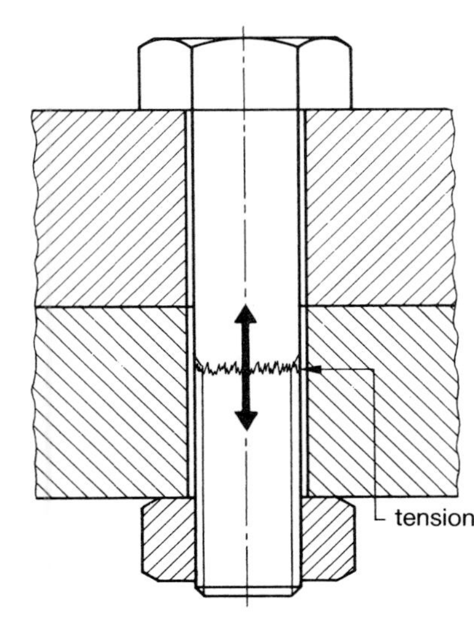

5.1 The bolt breaks

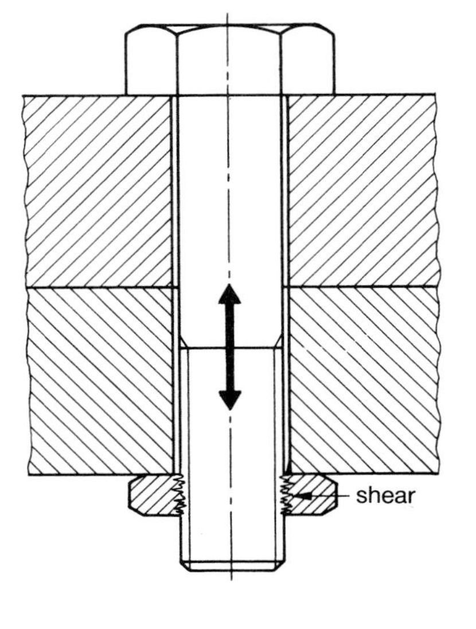

5.2 The nut shears off

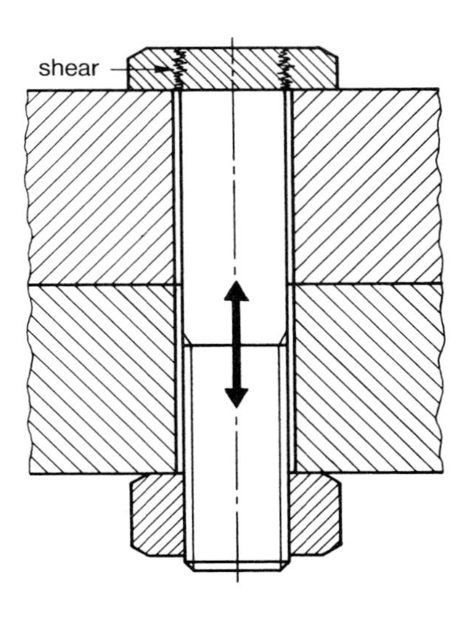

5.3 The bolt head shears off

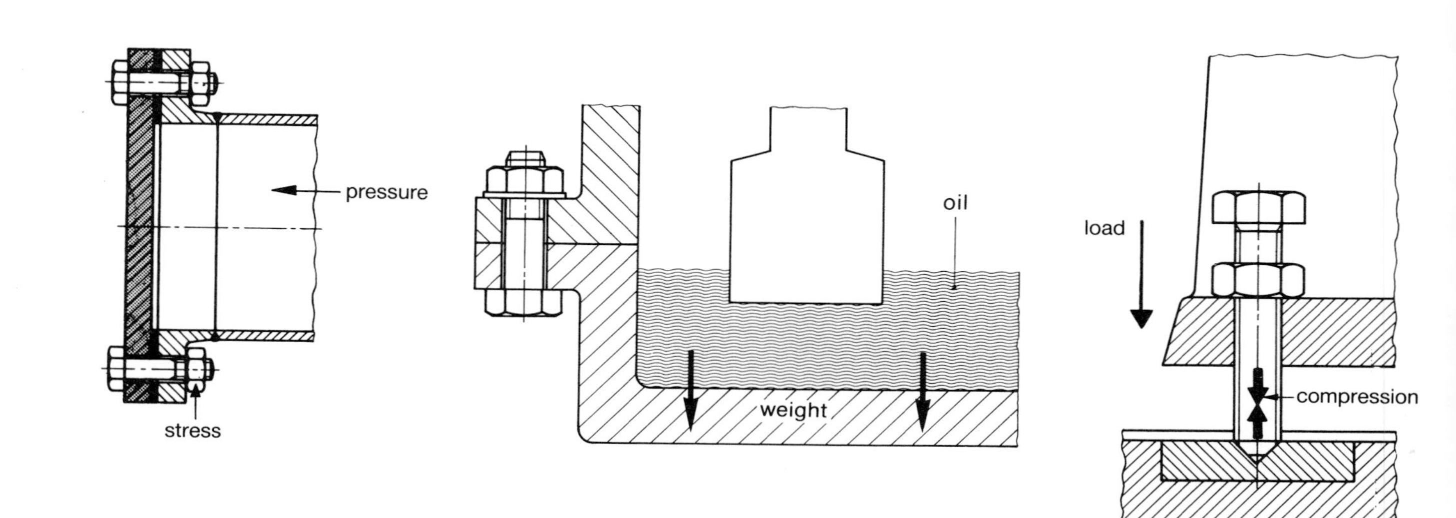

5.4 A blank flange

5.5 Weight causes tension

5.6 A levelling bolt

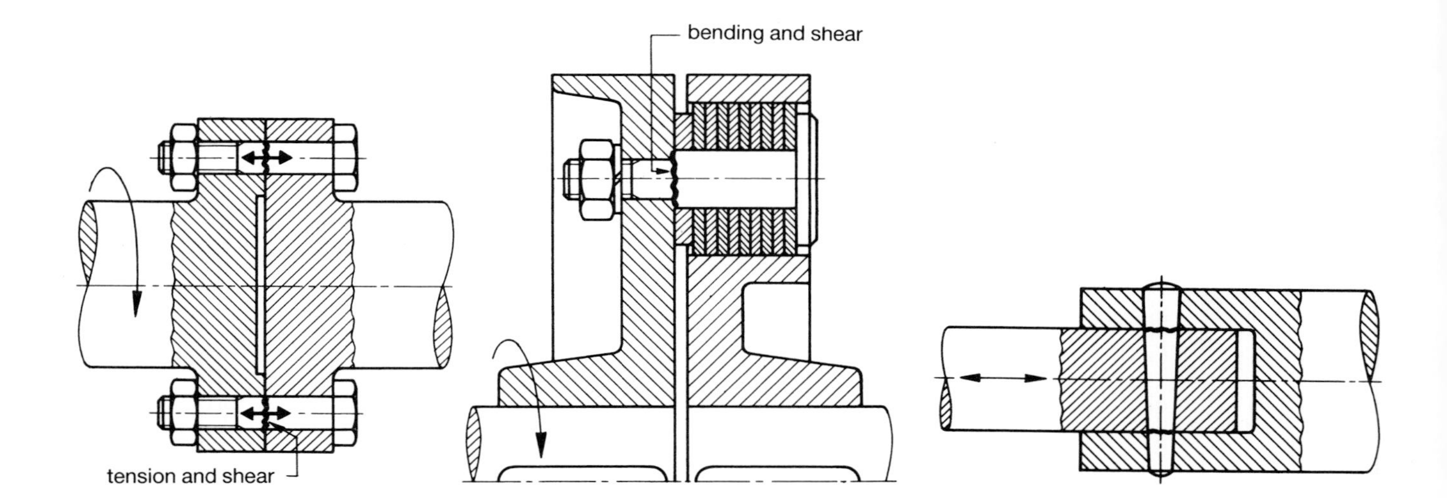

5.7 Shaft coupling

5.8 Flexible coupling

5.9 Taper pin

5.a.iii Shearing of threads – general

If the bolt and nut are made from the same material while the nut is of standard length (0.8 to 1.0 × dia.) the thread is capable of withstanding normal shear loads.
If the nut is shorter than the standard length, or is made of material with lower tensile strength, e.g. brass, the thread is liable to be sheared.

5.b Shear loads on pins or keys

Pins are subject to shear loads. Pinning is a simple method of securing which, in addition to preventing endwise movements between the parts (Fig. **5.**9) is also used to transmit moderate radial driving loads (Fig. **5.**10).
The key in Fig. **5.**11 is being subjected to a shear load along the length of contact. Keys and their attendant keyways are more expensive to produce than pinning, but can transmit relatively greater radial driving loads.

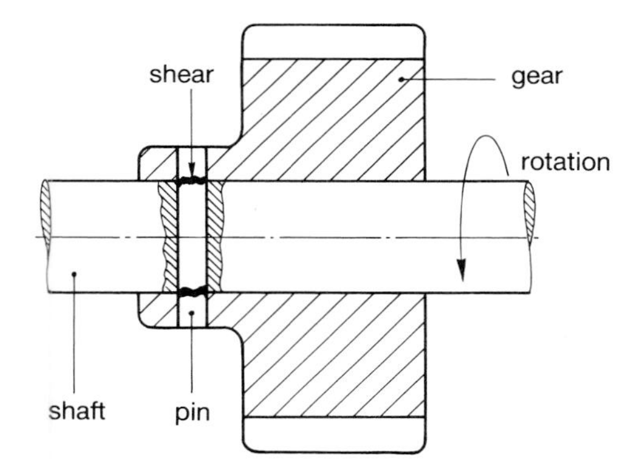

5.10 Gear held with a pin

5.c Effects of overtightening and distortion

Overtightening subjects the bolts or parts to excessive loads, resulting in breakage of bolts (Fig. **5.**1) or parts. Overtightening can also cause distortion. Distortion can cause permanent mis-shaping of parts and undue stresses to be set up in the assembly which may cause breakage (Fig. **5.**12). Control of these forces, exerted during the tightening process, is through the correct choice and use of tools. This is discussed in the next section.

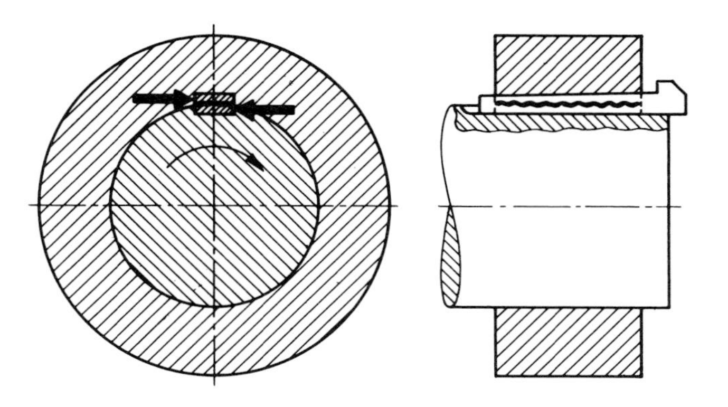

5.11 Gib headed taper key

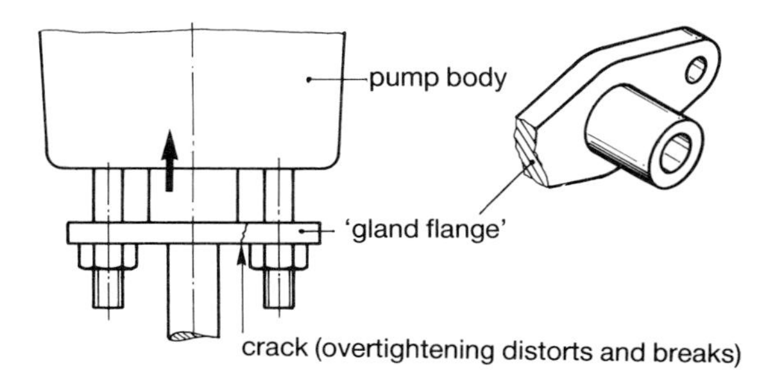

5.12 Cracked flange of water pump

6 Assembling and dismantling tools

6.a Application of turning moments and control of torque

Spanners (Fig. **6.**1) are used for tightening bolts and nuts. In doing so a turning moment or torque is exerted. This torque is applied to the bolt head or nut and is equal to the applied force multiplied by the length of the spanner (Fig. **6.**2).

For this reason:

- the length of the spanner is proportional to the size of the jaw; compare Figs. **6.**3a and **6.**3b
- a torque wrench (Fig. **6.**4) must be used if the magnitude of the torque is specified
- adjustable spanners should be used only at a leverage similar to that of the correctly fitting open-ended spanner for the same bolt or nut. Applying the right force to give the correct torque demands greater skill than when using the correct size spanner (Fig. **6.**5).
- the spanner jaw must fit bolts or nuts exactly if damage to them is to be avoided (Fig. **6.**6). For this reason the use of adjustable spanners is not recommended since the moveable jaw tends to create excessive clearance, thus causing damage to the nut or bolt head.

6.b Open-ended spanners

Figs. **6.**1a, **6.**2 and **6.**3 show open-ended spanners. These spanners have successive jaw sizes. The jaws of open-ended spanners are positioned at an angle to the centre line of the handle. This has been done to permit tightening of nuts even when the space available allows only for a short swing (Fig. **6.**7a-d). An open-ended spanner can be placed on the bolthead from the side as well as from above. It can be used with one hand.

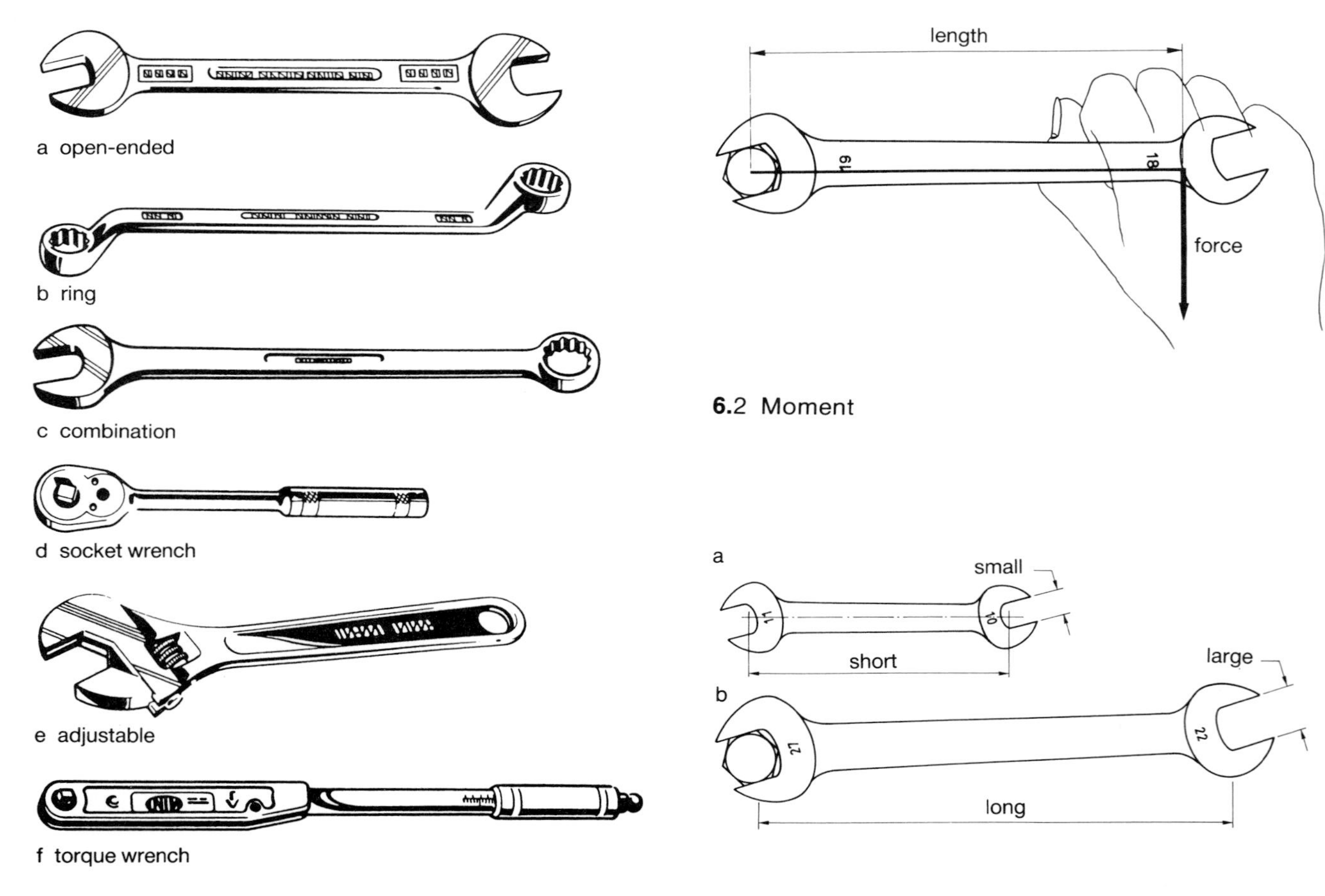

6.1 Spanners

6.2 Moment

6.3 Ratio of jaw size and length spanners

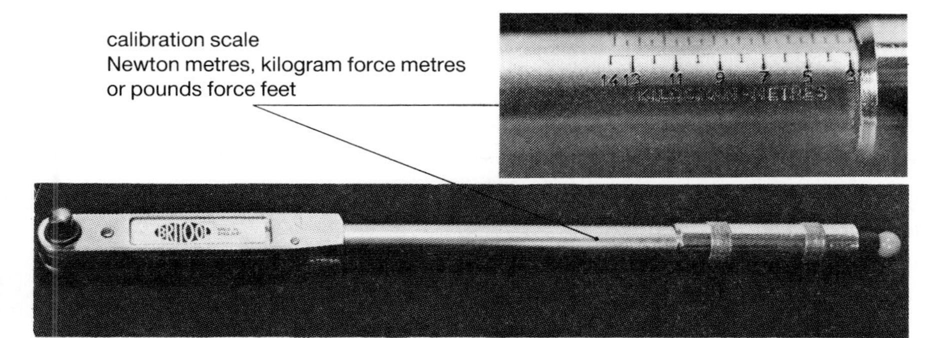

6.4 Torque wrench

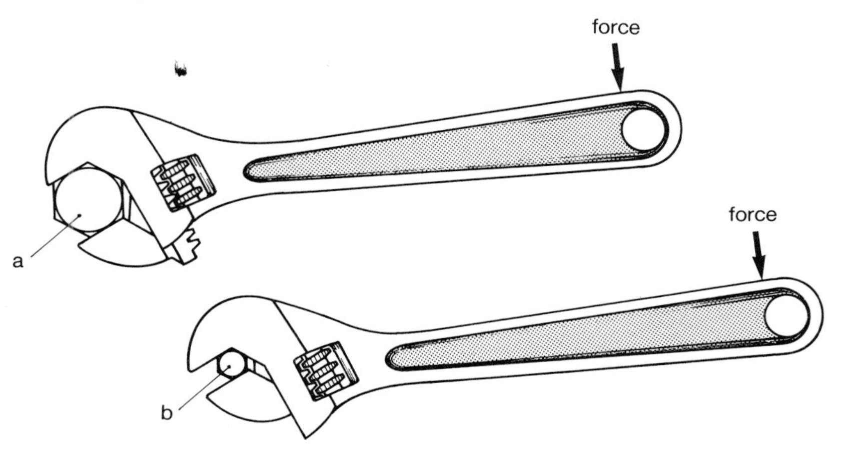

6.5 Adjustable spanners (less force required at b; same force could break bolt)

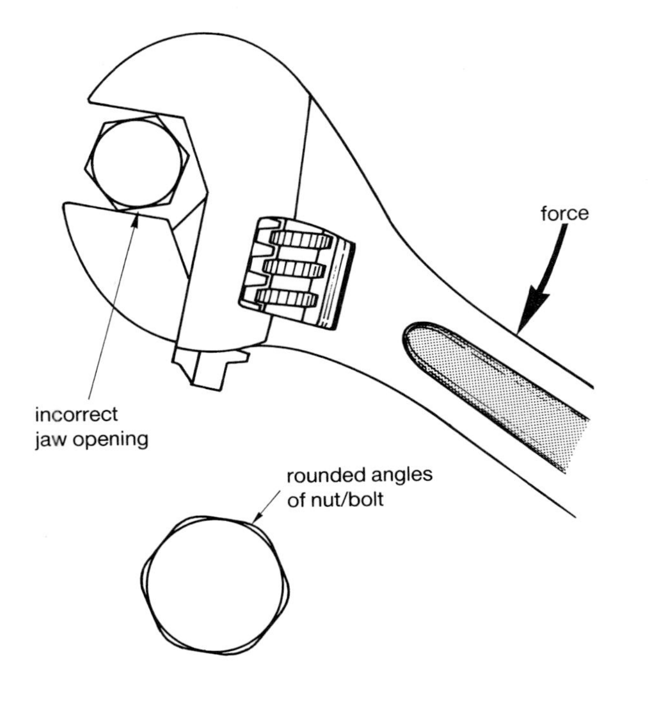

6.6 Damage to jaws/nut or bolt

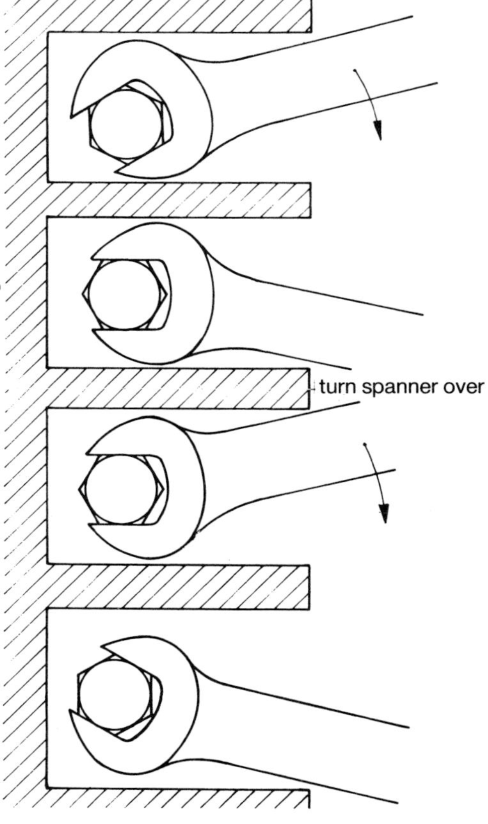

6.7 Using an open-ended spanner in a limited space

6.c Ring spanners and combination spanners

Both heads of the ring spanner in Fig. **6**.1b have an internal dodecagon, or hexagon, and as with the open-ended spanners, the sizes at each end are successive. Both heads are offset relative to the handle. A ring spanner can be placed on the nut or bolthead only from above and can be used with one hand.

Combination spanners as shown in Fig. **6**.1c have both an open end and a ring of the same size and can be used with one hand.

6.d Socket wrenches and torque wrenches

The basic socket wrench set consists of:

- a lever with a square tenon (Fig. **6**.8a and b)
- a number of sockets of different sizes (Fig. **6**.8c and d)

Each socket has an internal hexagon or dodecagon on one end and an internal square on the other to fit the square tenon on one end of a lever or extension piece (Fig. **6**.8e). The universal joint (Fig. **6**.8f) and extension piece make it possible to tighten nuts which are inaccessible for ring spanners and open-ended spanners. In some cases socket wrenches require two-handed application (Fig. **6**.9).

Torque wrenches must be used when the turning moment or torque is specified. Similar to a socket wrench, a torque wrench has a square driving tenon which fits into the square of a socket. The torque can be set at a prescribed amount by screwing in the end of the wrench handle (Fig. **6**.4.inset). A mechanism within the head of the spanner allows the handle to turn without applying more than the prescribed torque to the nut.

6.e Hexagon socket spanners

These spanners are made in different sizes (Fig. **6**.10a). They have a long and a short leg. The short leg is inserted into the socket of the bolt for final tightening (Fig. **6**.10c) since greater torque can be applied using the long leg as a lever, although it may be more convenient to use the longer end inserted into the bolt socket for assembly purposes (Fig. **6**.10.b).

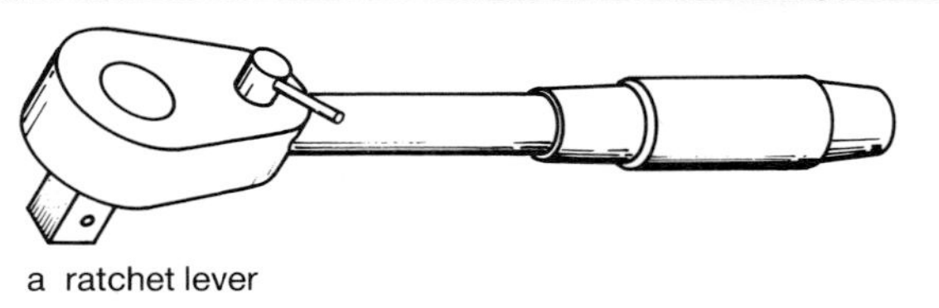

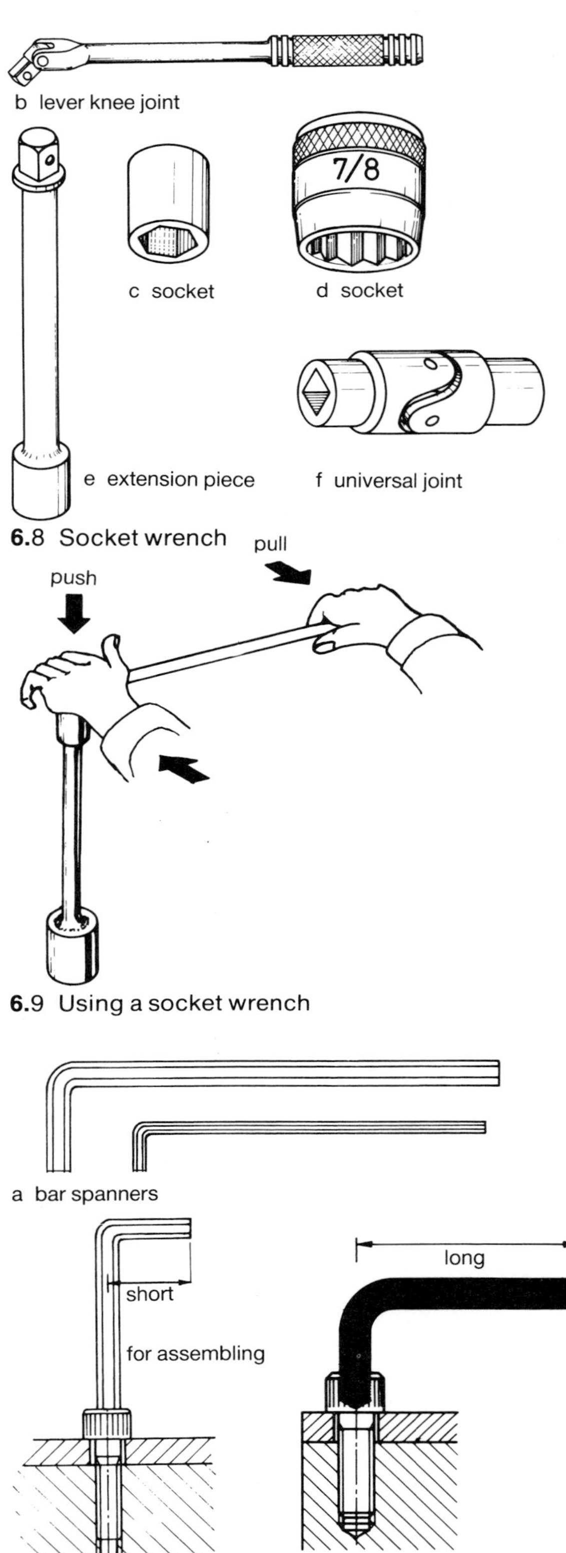

6.8 Socket wrench

6.9 Using a socket wrench

6.10 Hexagon socket bar spanner

6.f Impact wrench

This type of spanner has an internal hexagon on one end and a striking head on the other (Fig. **6.**11). The lever is very short and tightening or loosening a nut or bolt is achieved by striking the head. **Great care is required when using this tool, since striking too hard will cause the bolt to shear.**

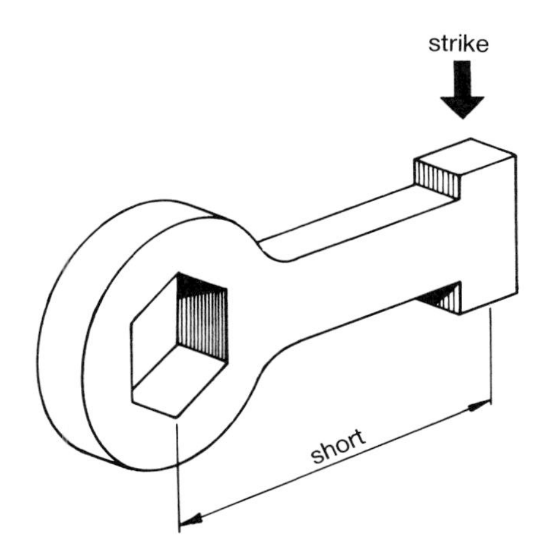

6.11 Striking spanner (Impact wrench)

6.g Lock spanners

As shown in Fig. **6.**12, these spanners are used to tighten circular nuts or threaded sleeves with holes or slots machined in them, to accept the spanner spur.

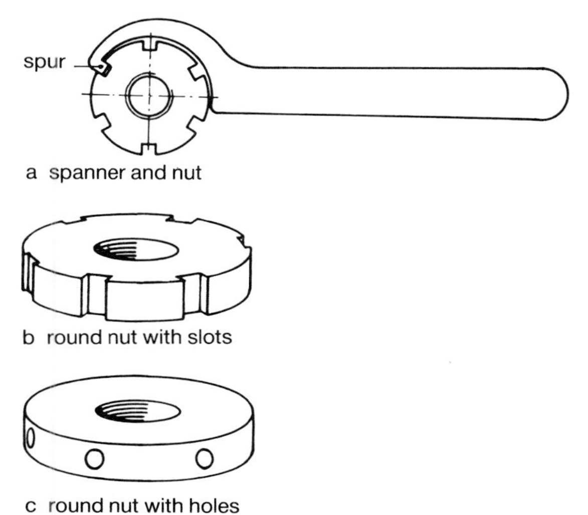

6.12 Lock spanner

6.h Adjustable spanners and pipe wrenches

The jaw size of adjustable spanners (Fig. **6.**1e) can be altered to different widths. As noted in Section 6.a they should be used with care and only when no correctly fitting spanner is available.

Pipe wrenches vary in type: the water pump pliers (Fig. **6.**13), pipe wrench (Fig. **6.**14) chain wrench (Fig. **6.**15) and stilson (Fig. **6.**16), are some of the many types used for assembling and dismantling pipework and fittings. They have hard and often specially shaped jaws, which enable them to grip the round pipe or pipefitting without slipping. **Pipe wrenches should not be used as spanners to tighten/loosen nuts or bolts.**

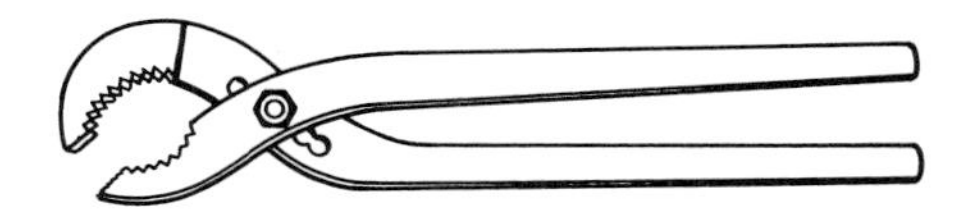

6.13 Water pump pliers

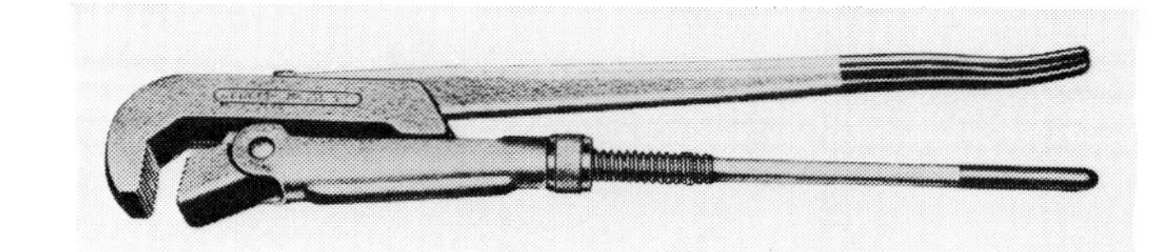

6.14 Pipe wrench

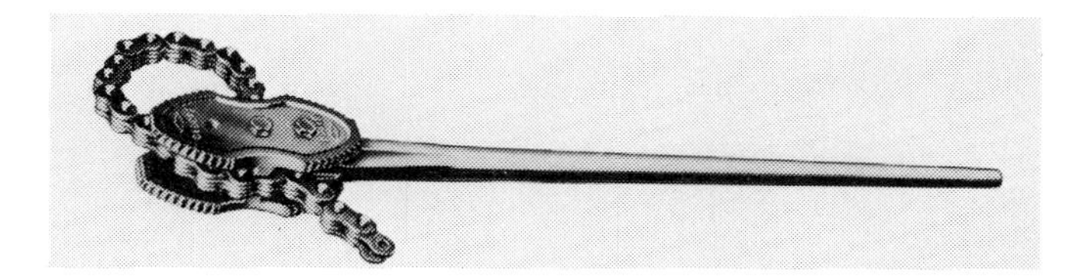

6.15 Chain wrench

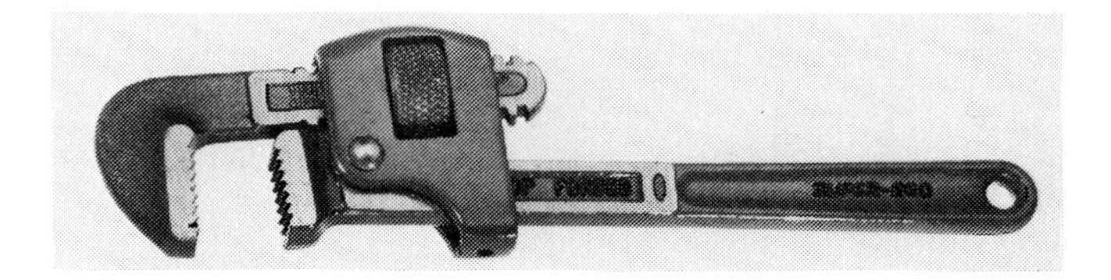

6.16 Stilson

6.i Screwdrivers

There are two main groups of screwdriver:

- flat blade screwdrivers (Fig. **6**.17a) for slotted screws (Fig. **6**.18)
- cross head screwdrivers (Fig. **6**.19a) for cross recessed screws (Fig. **6**.19b).

The following should be taken into account when using flat blade screwdrivers:

- the width of the blade should be correct (Fig. **6**.20a, b and c).
- the thickness of the blade should be correct (Fig. **6**.21a and b).

As with the flat blade, the cross head screwdriver must fit the head of the screw properly. Both types of screwdriver are made in a wide variety of sizes.

Impact screwdrivers are available (Fig. **6**.17b). These contain a heavy spring which holds the screwdriver bit extended. A blow with a hammer on the striking surface causes the spring to compress and impart a rotary motion to the blade.

Caution

Care must be exercised when using an impact screwdriver. A carelessly delivered blow could result in damage to components.

handle
ferrule
shank|
shank length
blade

a flat blade

force
striking surface
body
driver bit
rotation

b impact driver

6.17 Screwdrivers

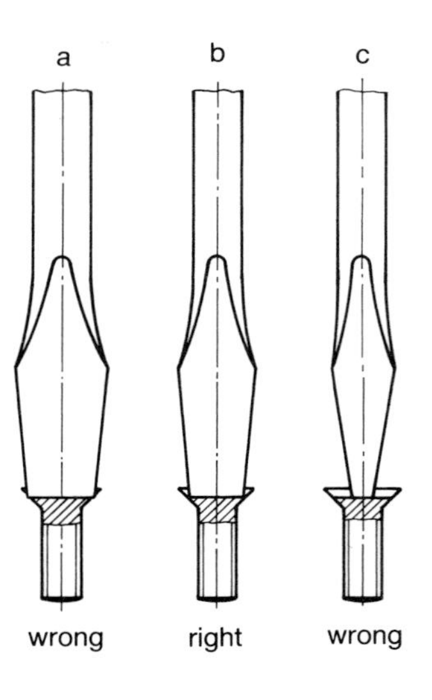

6.20 Illustration of screw-drivers to fit screw-head-width of blade

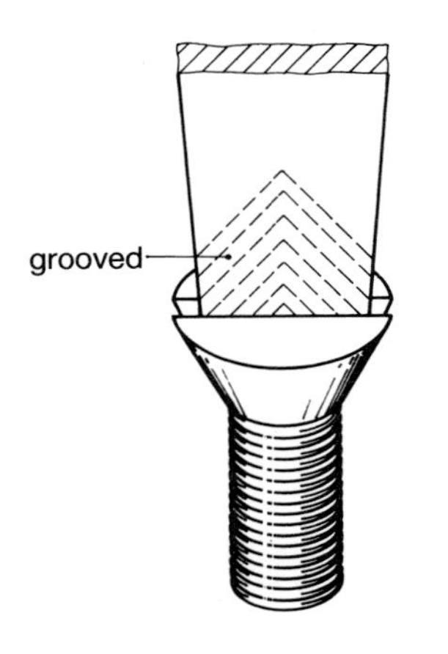

6.18 Slotted screw

a cross head driving point

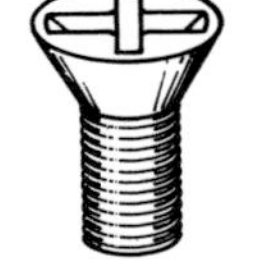

b cross recessed screw

6.19 Cross headed screwdriver and screw

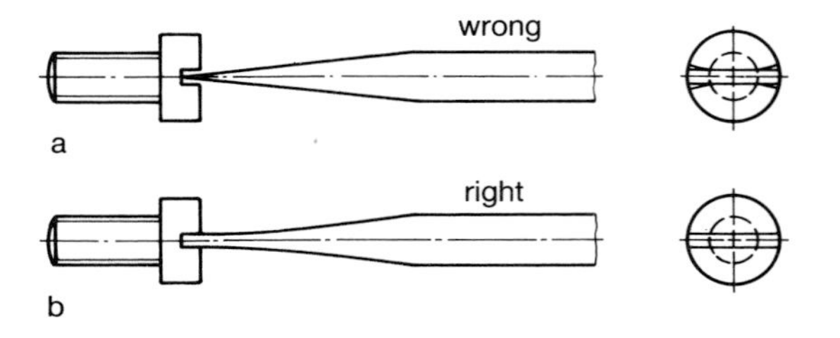

6.21 Illustration of screwdriver to fit screwhead slot-blade thickness

6.j Pliers

Pliers (Fig. **6.**22) are used for gripping, squeezing, manipulating, cutting, pulling, etc., in the assemblingand dismantling process. Pliers use the lever principle to magnify the force applied. In Fig. **6.**23, the applied force will be multiplied 10 times at the cutting or gripping point.

The shape of the jaws decides the type of application; those shown in Fig. **6.**22d and e are used for circlip manipulations while those in Fig. **6.**22c and f are long or snipe-nosed pliers for gripping or manipulating in awkward or confined spaces or for light instrument work.

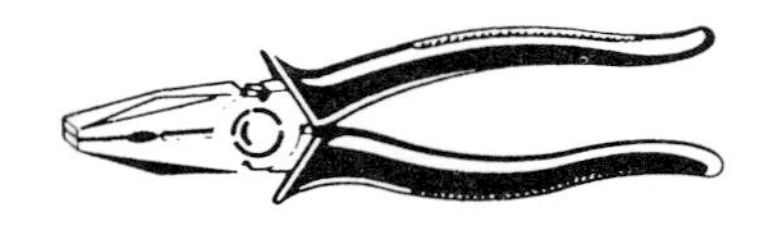

a general purpose pliers

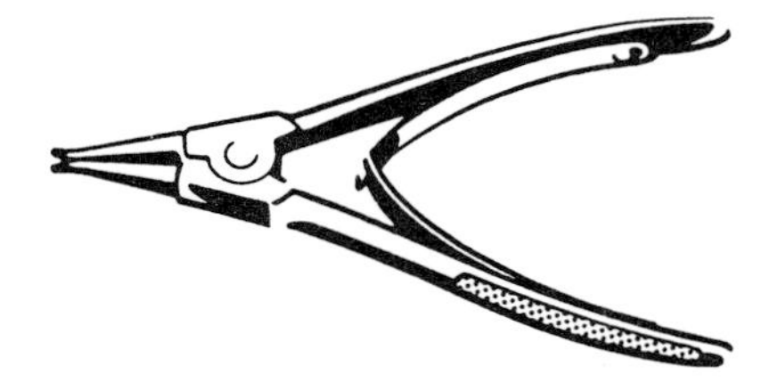

d circlip pliers

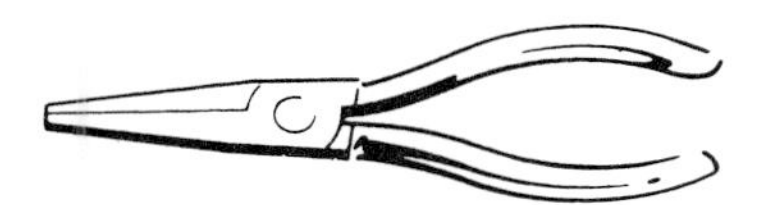

b insulated pliers

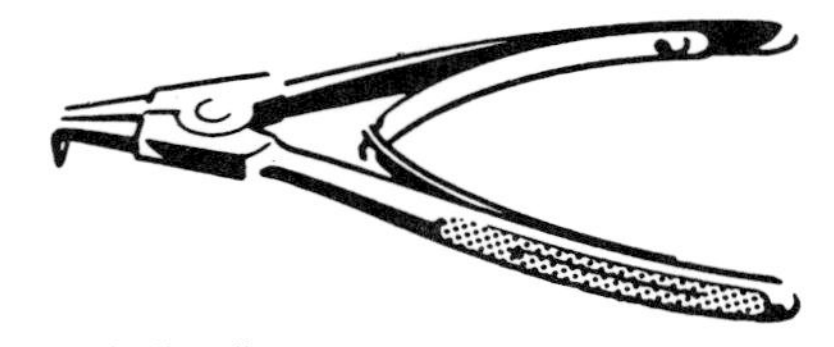

e circlip pliers

c long nose pliers

f snipe-nosed pilers

6.22 Types of pliers

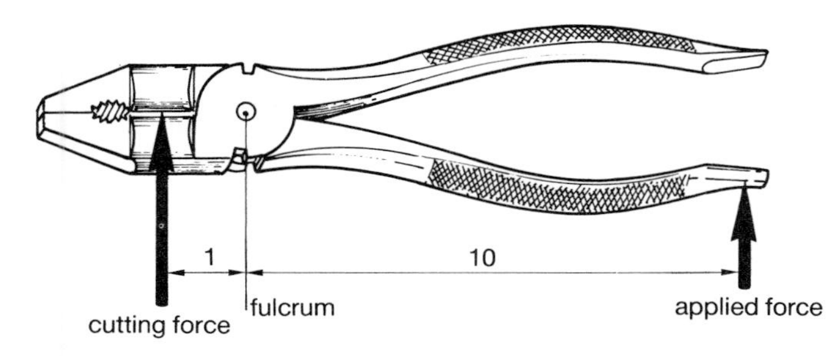

6.23 Pliers use the lever principle

6.k Hammers

Hammers are used for many kinds of percussive (striking) tasks during assembling and dismantling. As can be seen in Fig. **6.**24 there are variations in shape, mass and material according to the application. The weight of head and length of shaft influence the striking force possible. The energy may be transferred to the work directly or via another tool (e.g. a pin punch Fig. **6.**25). A shock load is sometimes more effective and easier to apply than an even pressure.

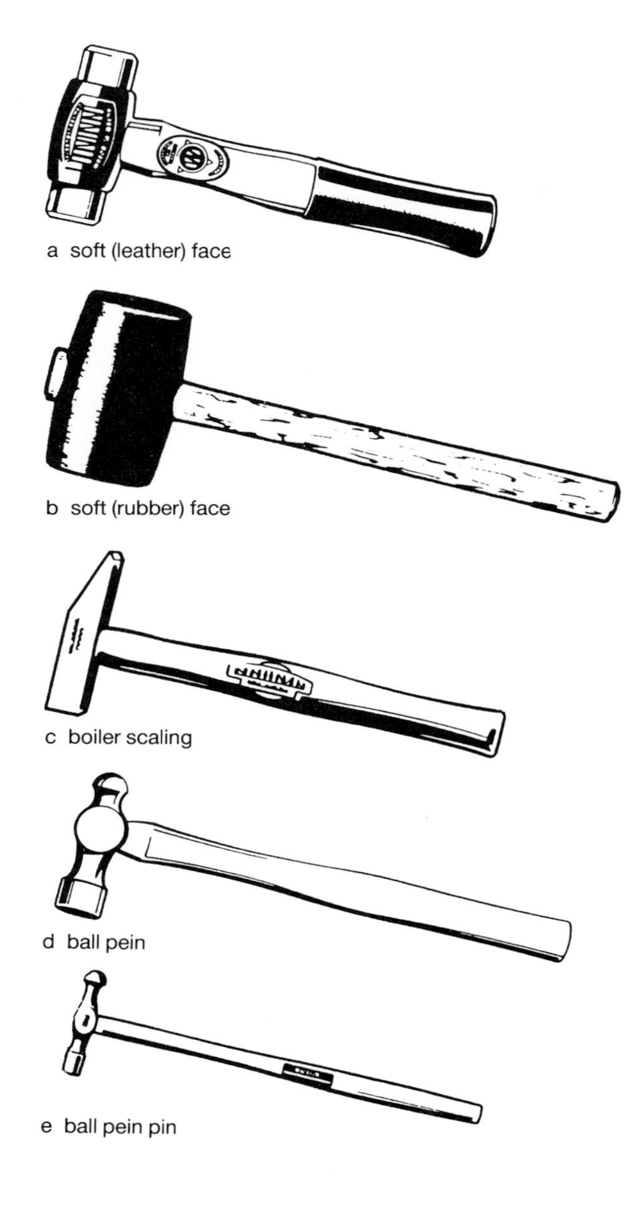

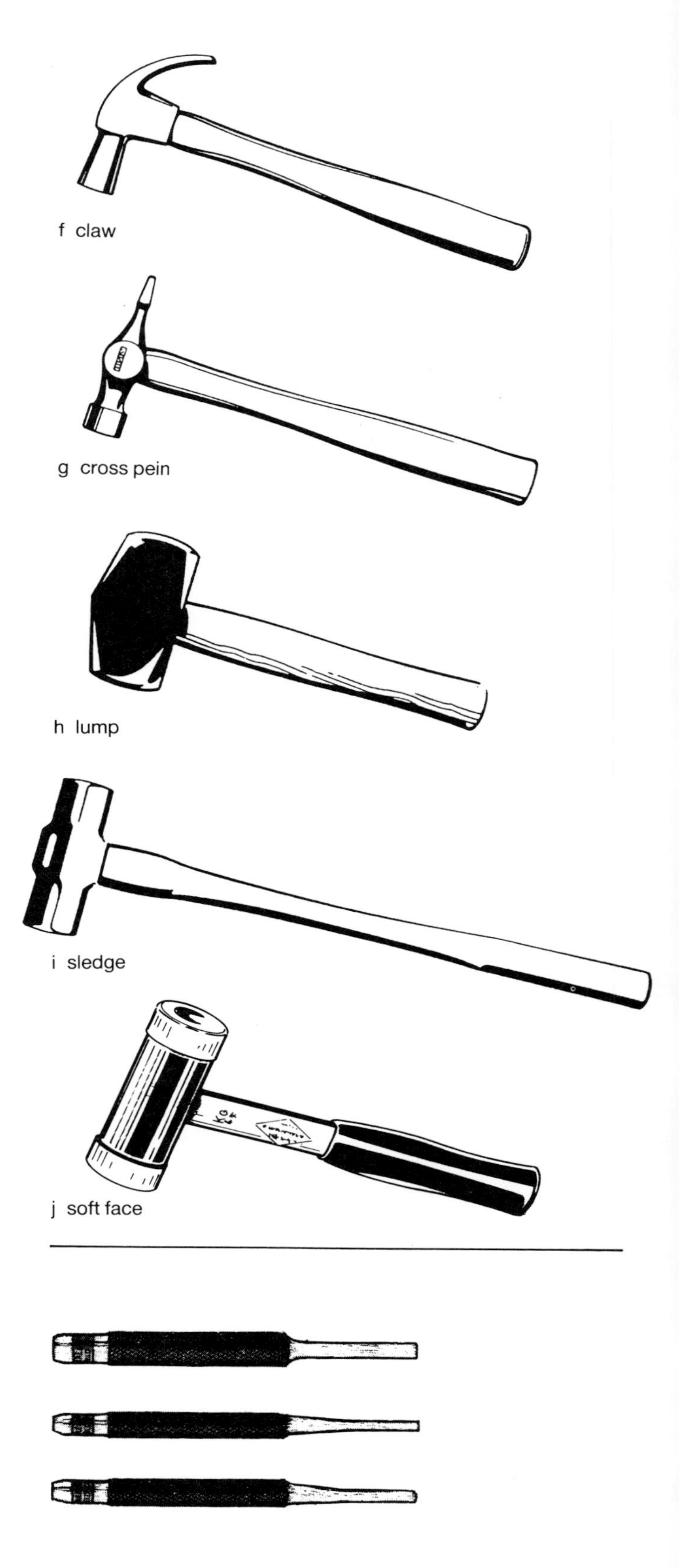

6.24 Hammers

6.25 Pin punches

6.1 Levers and supports

Levers (Fig. **6**.26) are used for lifting and separating in assembling and dismantling applications; they work on the same principle as that applied to pliers, i.e. the greater the length of the lever then the more force can be applied to lift the load. As the movement of the load is usually small, supports (Fig. **6**.27) are used in conjunction with the levers.

Fig. **6**.28 shows a 1 tonne machine that has been lifted so that the jack can be used. Note that both levers and supports should be able to support the weights concerned with relative ease. It is safe practice to place suitable safety packing or chocks under the load as it is lifted when using jacks, so reducing the hazard should the jack fail or the load move. **Extreme care should be taken to ensure that neither you nor any colleague works or reaches under the lifted weight until it is safely supported.**

a wedge (hardwood/steel)

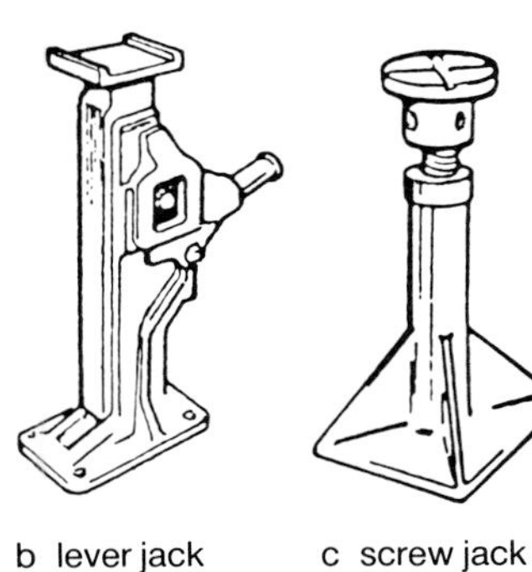

b lever jack

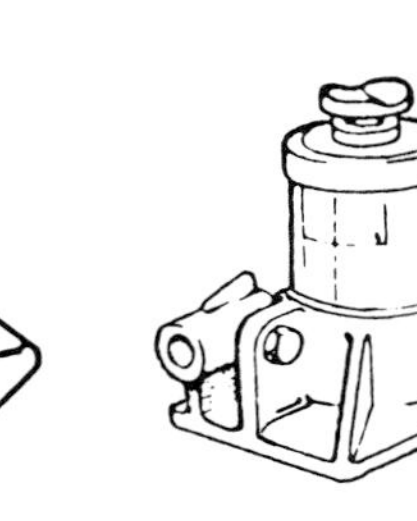

c screw jack

d hydraulic jack

6.27 Supports

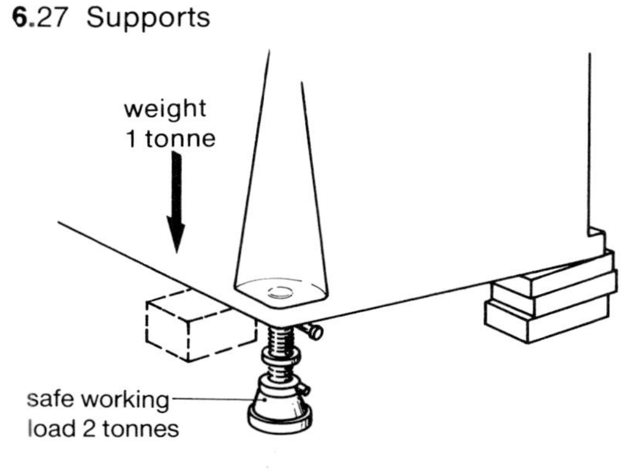

6.28 Lifting a 1 tonne machine

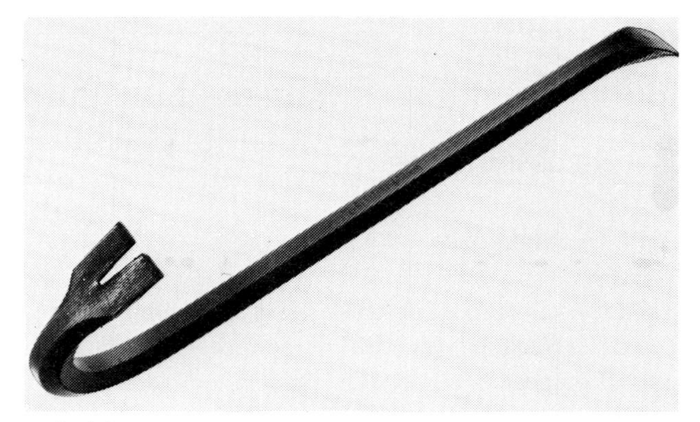

a pinch bar

b crow bar

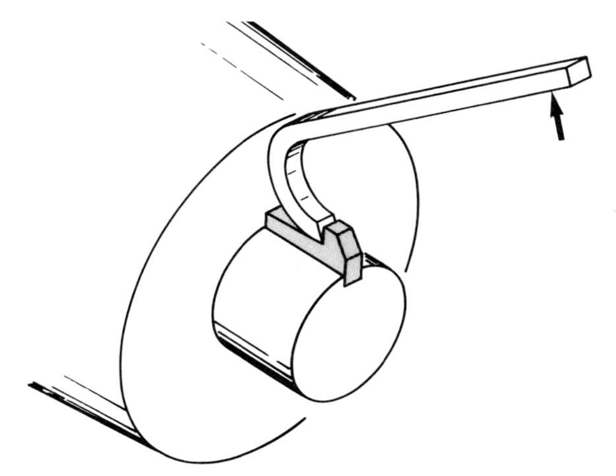

c jumbo

d podger bar

6.26 Levers

7 Purpose of tools and devices used

7.a In assembling

7.a.i Common tools

The form and purpose of tools used in assembling was discussed in Section 6, so will not be repeated here. Their overall purpose is to make the assembly of parts into the complete whole both possible and efficient.

7.a.ii Joining devices

These devices, such as screws, nuts, bolts (Fig. **7**.1 and **7**.2), keys (Fig. **7**.3) and pins (Fig. **7**.4) are used to join one part of an assembly to another. They include the use of adhesives (Fig. **7**.5a and **7**.5b) and as has been shown in earlier sections, the choice is influenced by the nature of the joint involved. The choice is also controlled by the likelihood of needing to break the joint during the service life of the part.

7.a.iii Locking devices

These are mostly used to prevent the parts previously discussed from working loose during service. Typical examples are shown in Fig. **7**.6. Adhesives are sometimes used to prevent such movement.

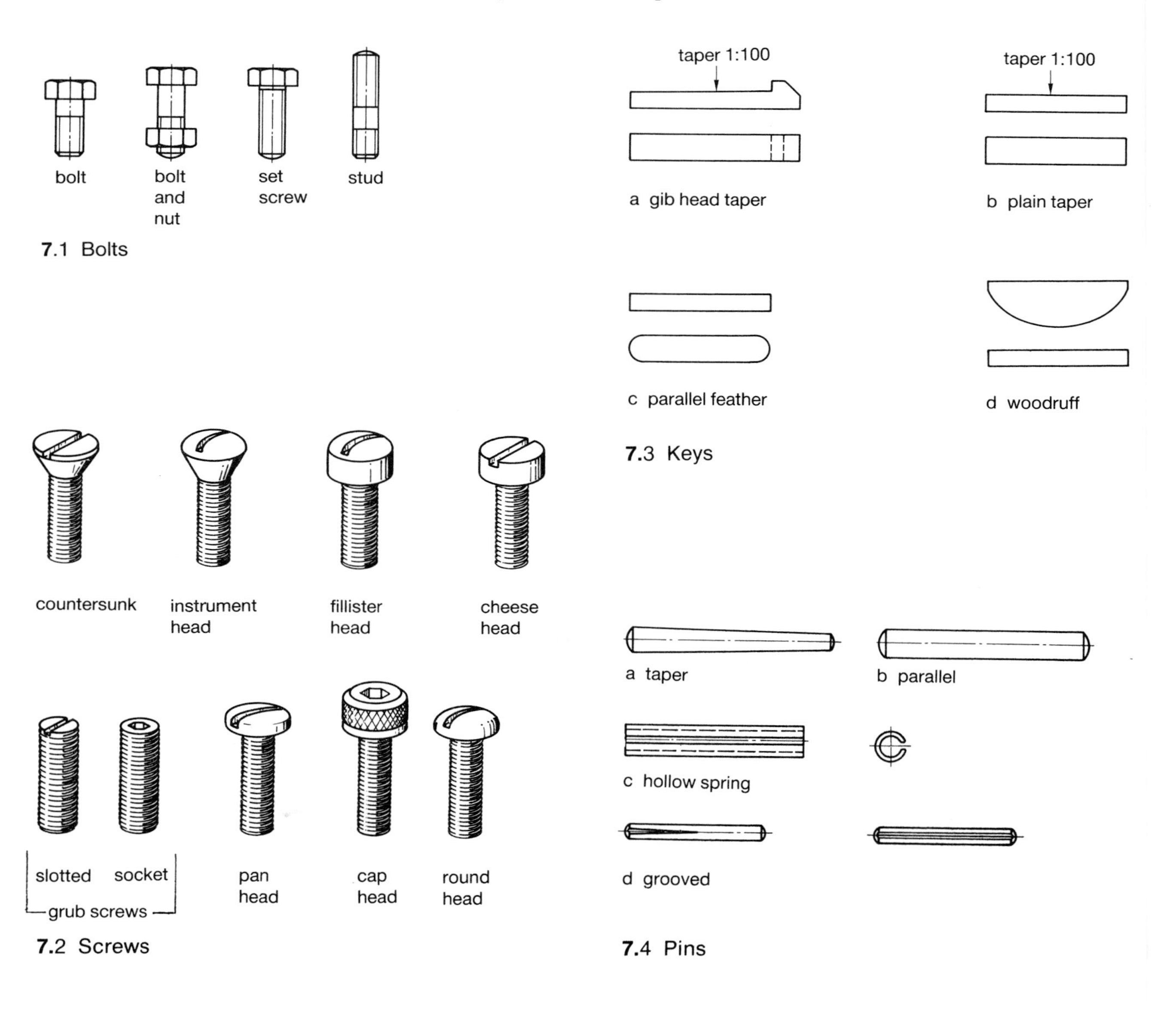

7.1 Bolts

7.2 Screws

7.3 Keys

7.4 Pins

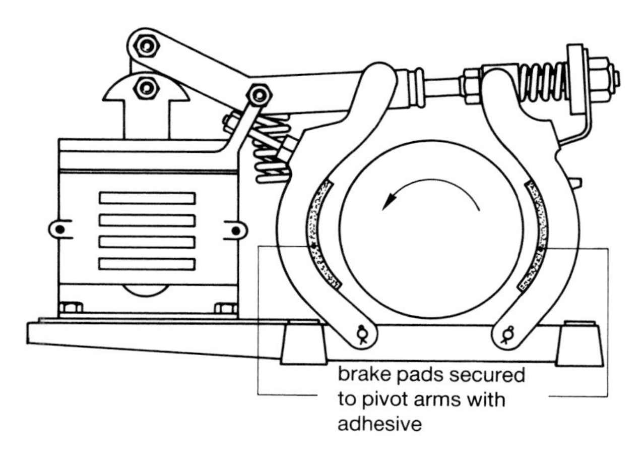

a brake pads in a solenoid operated brake

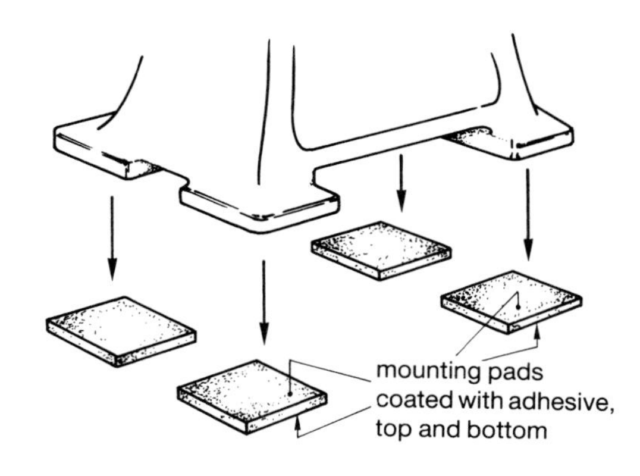

b floor mounted machine secured with adhesive; using differing thicknesses of pads, if required, for levelling

7.5 Use of adhesives

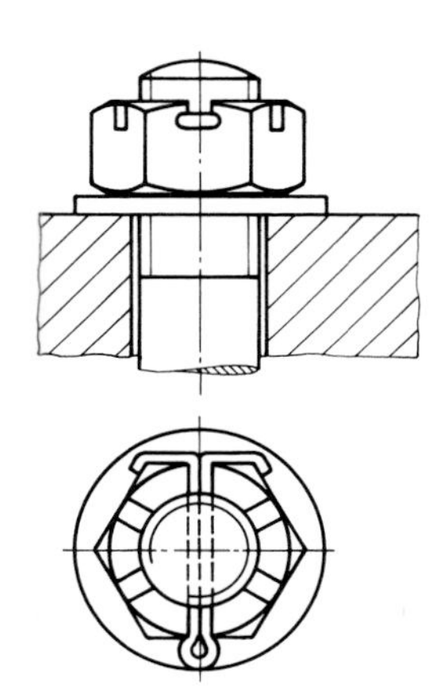

a castle nut with split pin

b slotted nut with split pin

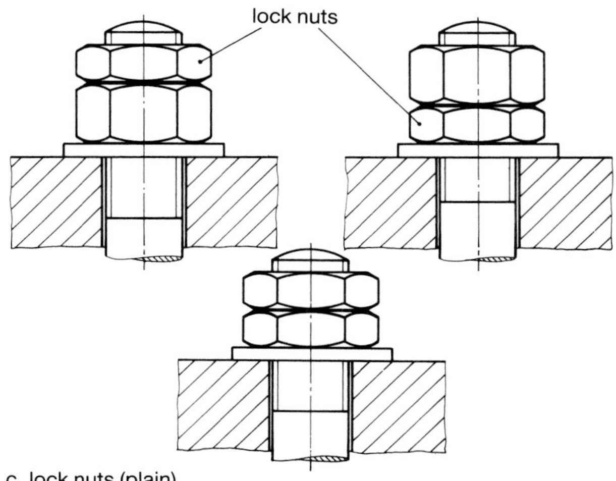

c lock nuts (plain)

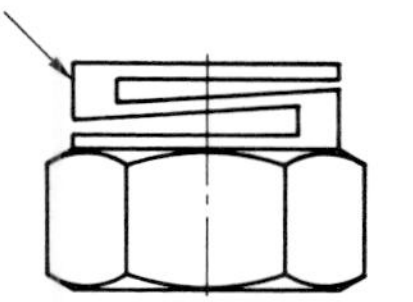

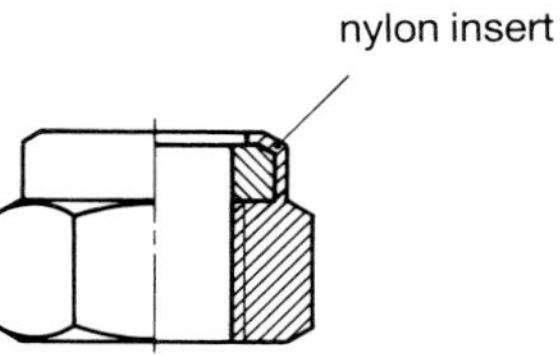

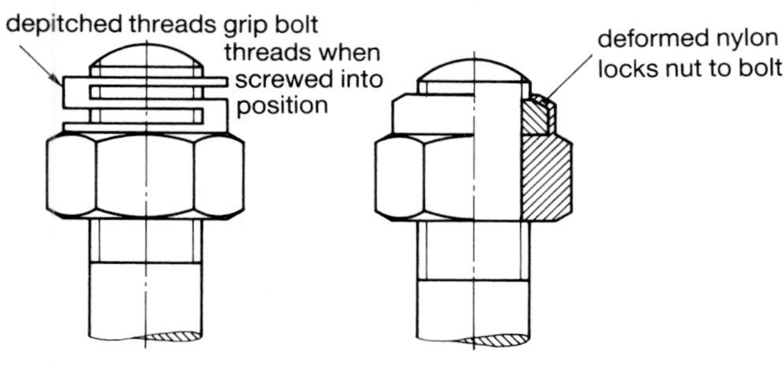

d lock nuts (self locking)

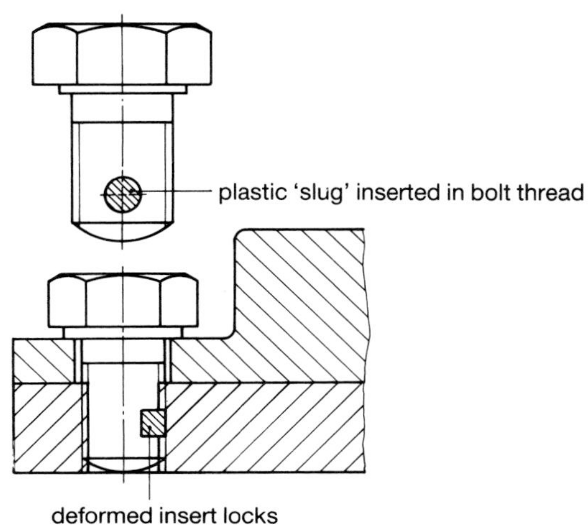

e self locking set screws or bolt

7.6 Locking devices

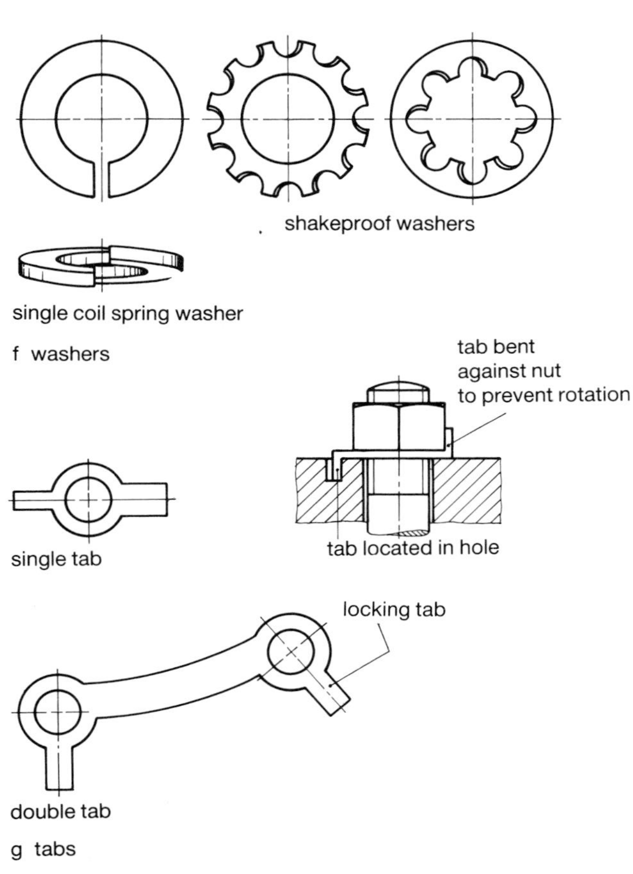

f washers

g tabs

7.6 Locking devices (continued)

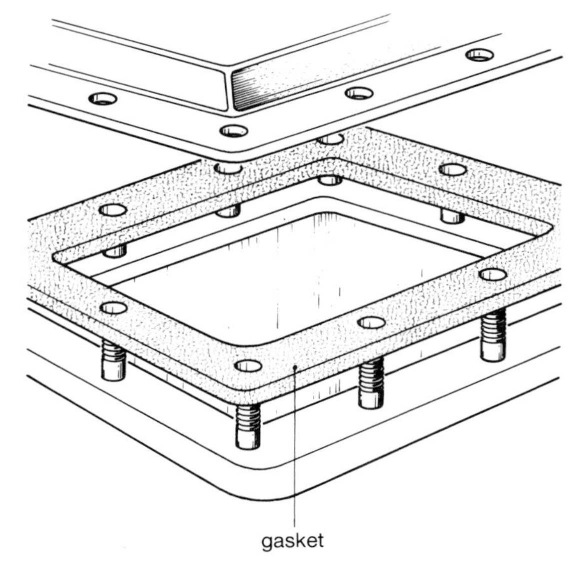

a flange joint (gasket packing)

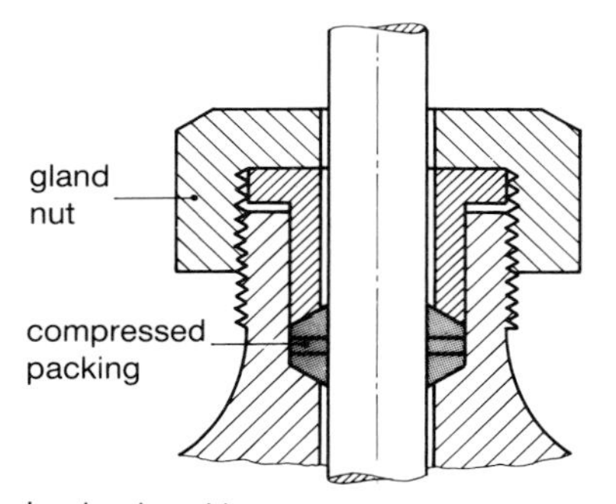

b gland packing

7.a.iv Sealing devices

These are used to make parts or joints in assemblies fluid or gas tight. Fig. **7**.7 shows each of the following types:

- plate packings or gaskets (Fig. **7**.7a)
- stuffing and gland packing (Fig. **7**.7b)
- 'o' rings and square section seals (Fig. **7**.7c)
- lip seals (Fig. **7**.7d)
- boot seals (Fig. **7**.7e)
- mechanical seals (Fig. **7**.7f)

Many more types of seal are available and care must be taken to choose the type suited to the operating conditions i.e. the mating materials, the pressure, temperature and nature of the fluid or gas involved.

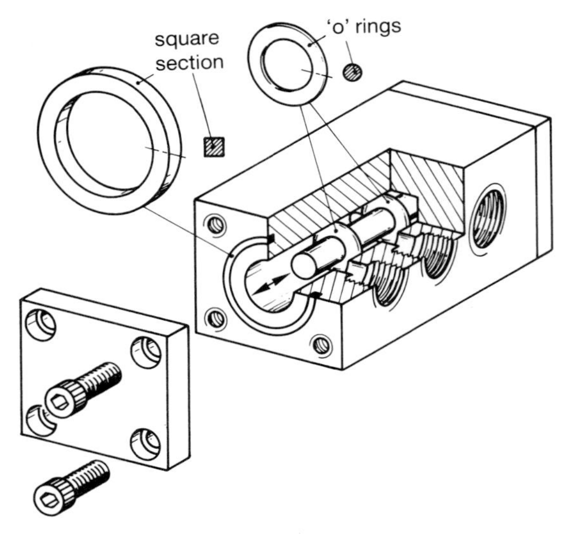

c pneumatic spool valve with 'o' ring seals

7.7 Sealing devices

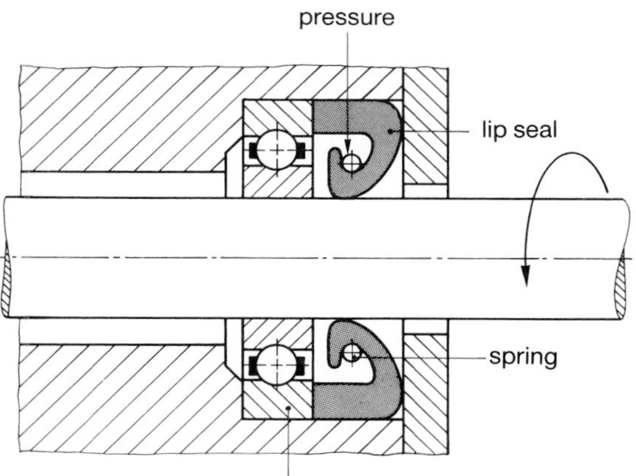

d lip seal

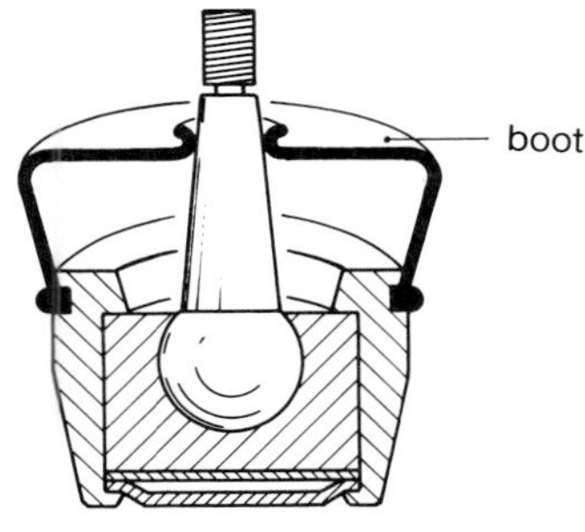

e boot seal

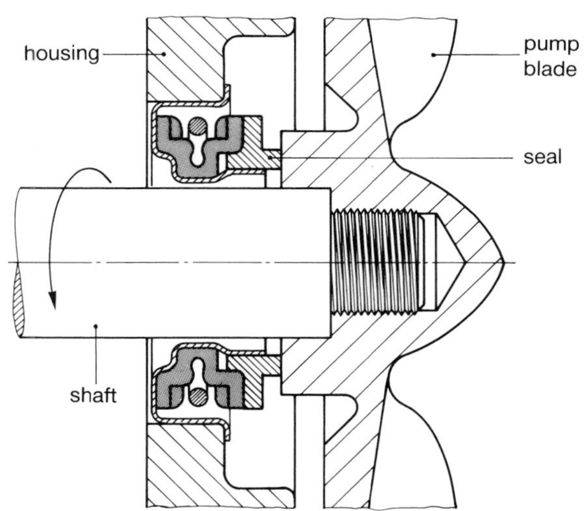

f mechanical seal

7.7 Sealing devices (continued)

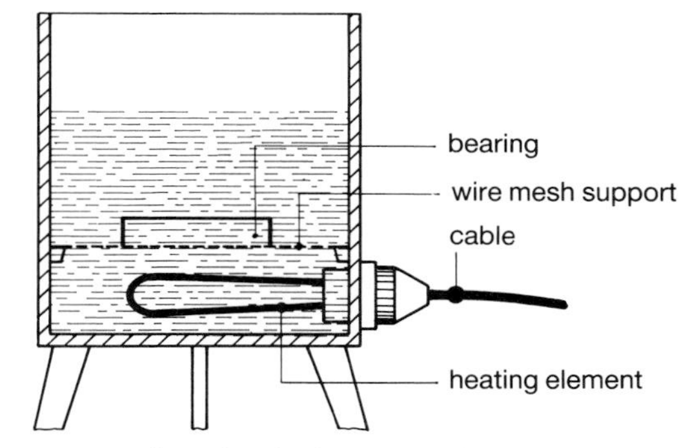

a expanding a bearing in an oil bath

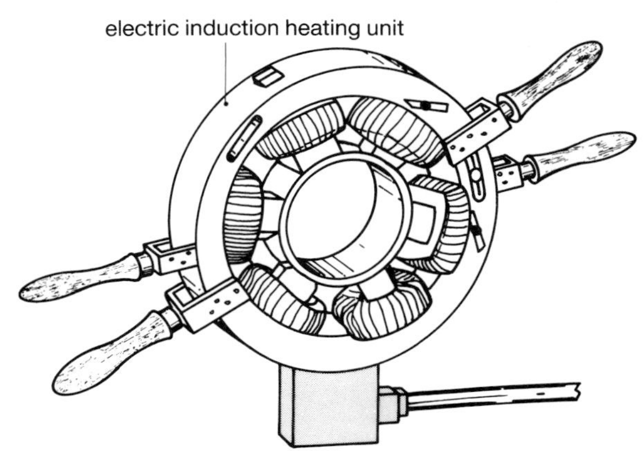

b expanding a bearing using an induction heater

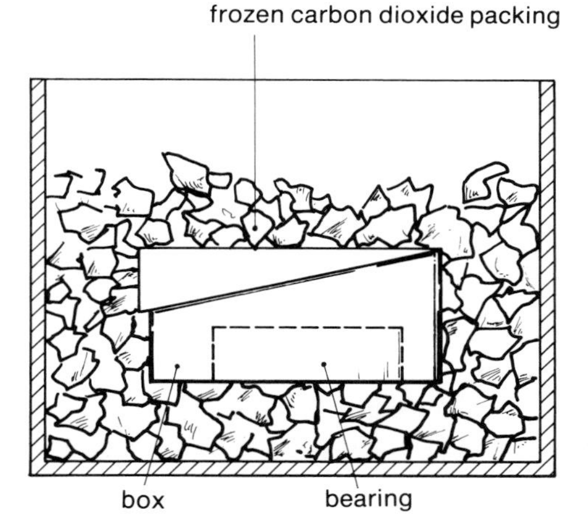

c bearing being contracted using freeze technique

7.8 Shrink joining equipment

7.a.v Equipment for shrink joining

The basic equipment falls into the following types:

- expansion: oil baths and induction coils (Fig. **7**.8a and b) where the bearing is heated to approximately 100°C, then fitted to the shaft. When the bearing cools the joint has the correct interference fit.
- contraction; refrigeration units, dry ice (Fig. **7**.8c), where the shaft (or bearing) is cooled and then fitted to the bearing (or housing). When the cooled part returns to normal temperature the joint has the correct interference fit.

Safety equipment, such as gloves and goggles, must be used during these operations.

7.a.vi Presses

Both mechanical and hydraulic presses (Fig. 7.9a and b) may be used in assembling where interference fits are encountered. By producing even and controlled pressure, presses safely overcome the resistance between the mating parts and enable them to be positioned accurately.

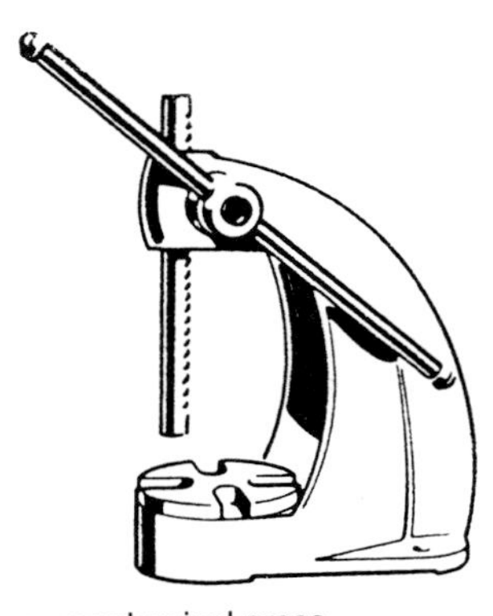

a mechanical press

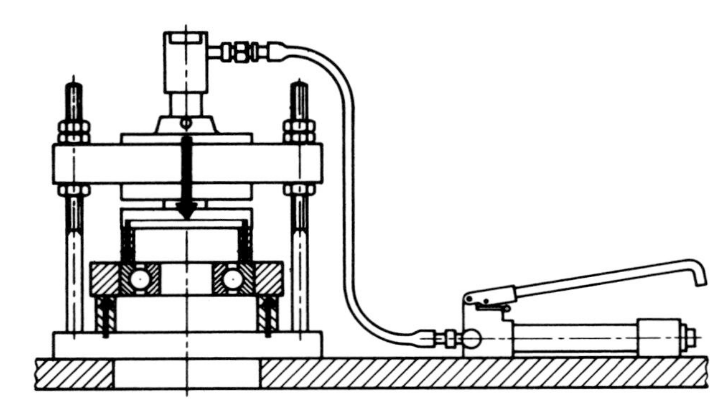

b hydraulic press

7.9 Presses

7.a.vii Measuring and testing equipment

- Rules, verniers, micrometers and depth gauges can be used to check both size and position of components before and during assembly (Fig. 7.10a-d).
- Spirit levels and plumb lines are used to establish or check horizontal and vertical datums (Fig. 7.11a-d).
- Angles can be checked or set with protractors or clinometers (Fig. 7.12a-b).
- Clearances can be set or checked by feeler gauges (Fig. 7.13).
- Concentricity can be checked using dial indicators (Fig. 7.14).
- Straight edges are used for checking or setting straight lines on or between components (Fig. 7.15).

Such equipment is usually selected according to the limits of accuracy prescribed for the assembly and the accessibility of the equipment. More information can be found in the series book title *Measuring and Marking Out*.

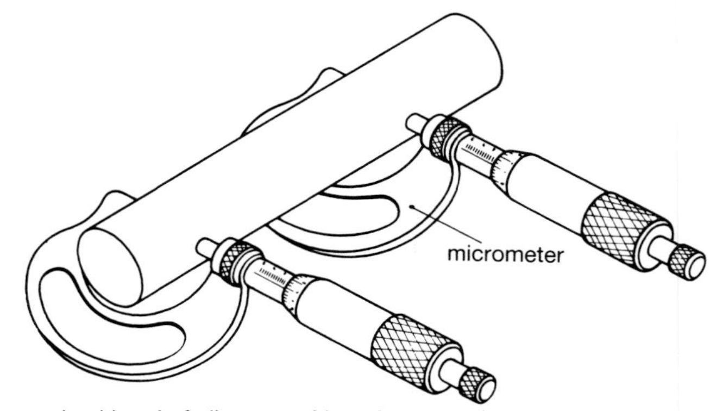

a checking shaft diameter with a micrometer (to accuracy of 0.01 mm)

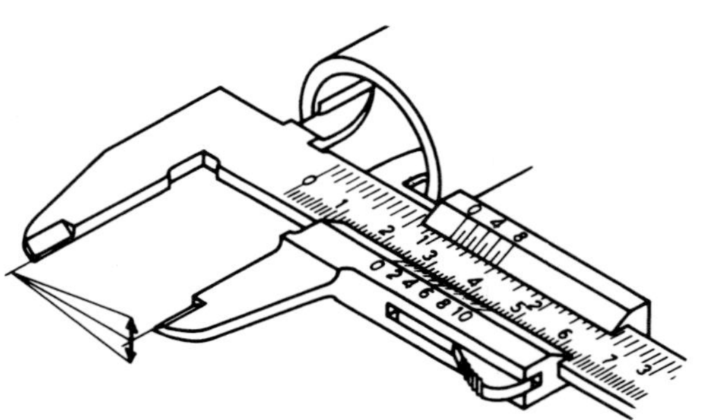

b checking base size with a vernier caliper (to accuracy of 0.02 mm)

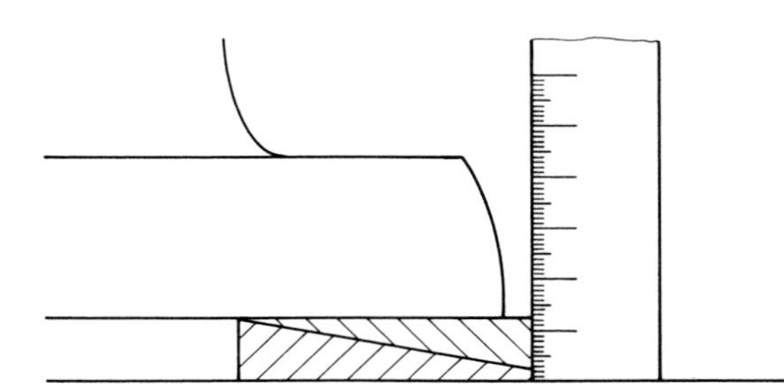

c checking size of packing needed with a rule (to accuracy of 0.5 mm)

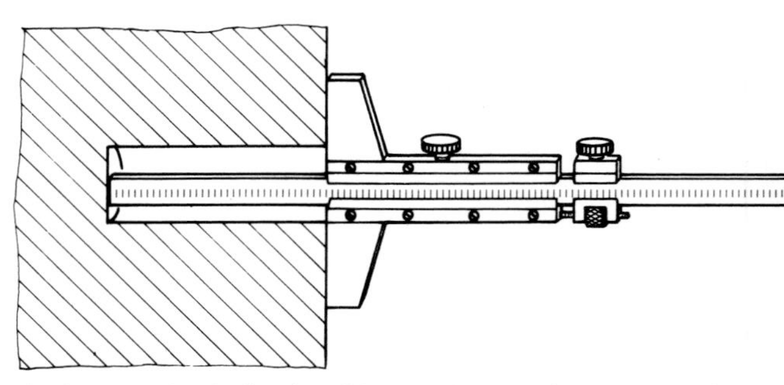

d checking depth of a slot with a depth gauge (to accuracy of 0.02 mm)

7.10 Use of linear measuring devices

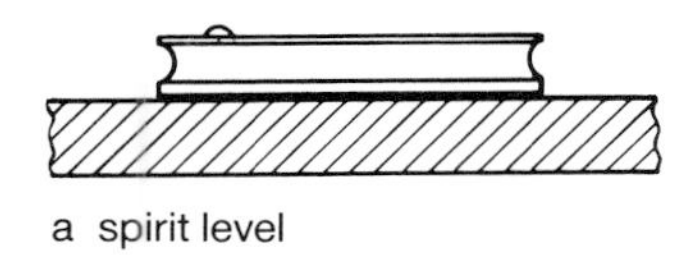

a spirit level

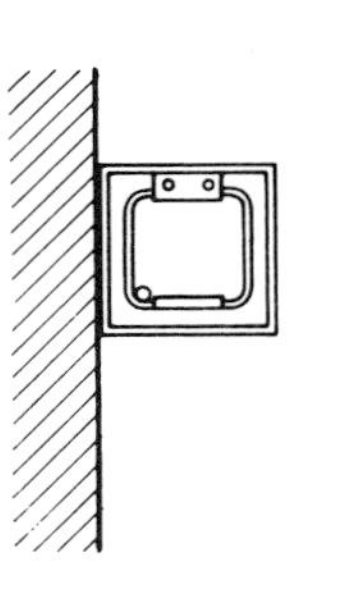

b box level

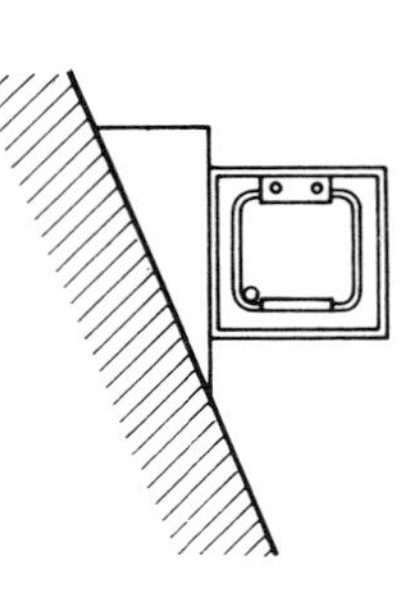

c box level

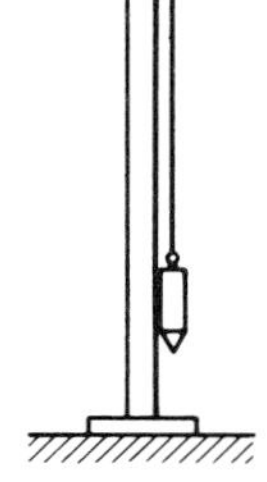

d plumb line

7.11 Establishing and checking horizontal and vertical lines

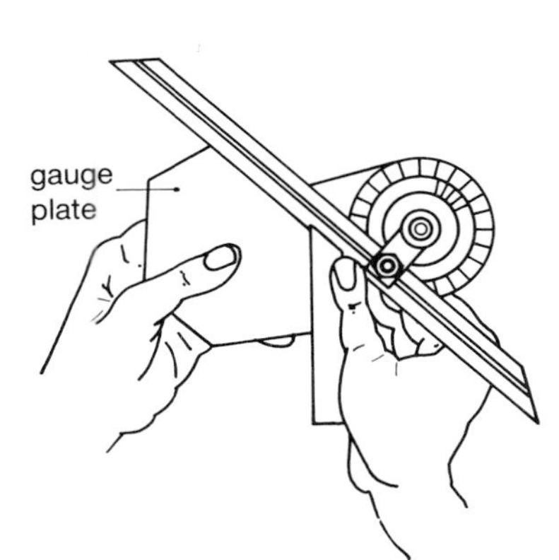

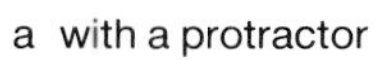

a with a protractor

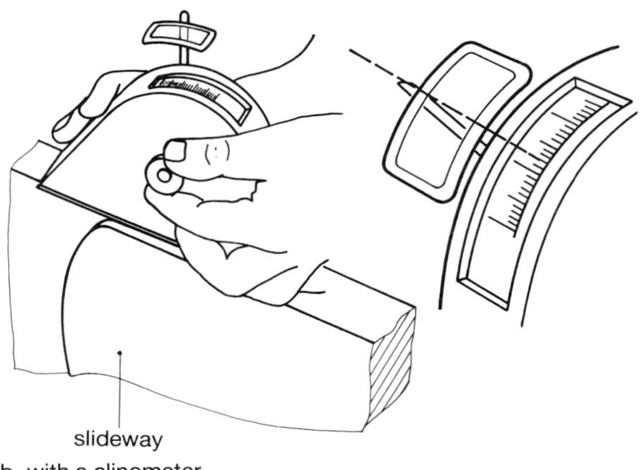

b with a clinometer

7.12 Setting or checking angles

7.13 Measuring clearance

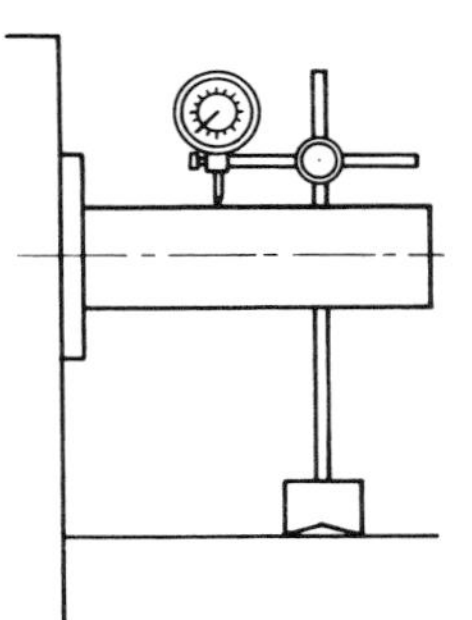

7.14 Checking for concentricity

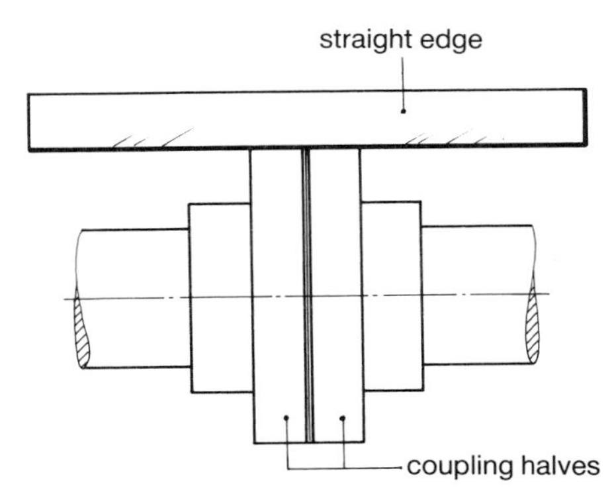

7.15 Checking for straightness

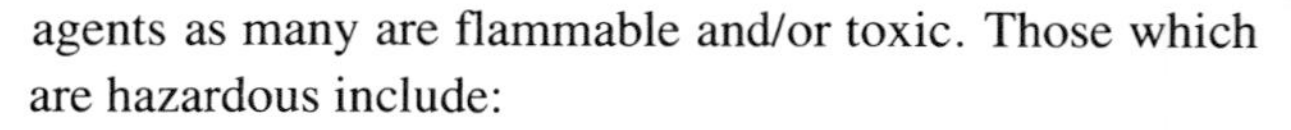

7.b In dismantling

7.b.i Common tools

The form and purpose of tools used in dismantling was discussed in Section 6 so will not be repeated here. Their overall purpose is to make dismantling procedures safe and efficient.

7.b.ii Cleansing agents

These are used to remove grease, oil, scum, or any other process material from the part to be dismantled. This allows the parts to be inspected and dismantled more efficiently. Occasionally parts cannot be cleaned until dismantling has taken place, but in all cases the parts must be carefully treated and stored, i.e. rusting and dust penetration is prevented by the use of oil, grease and clean covers etc. (Fig. **7**.16).

Care must also be taken in the storage and use of cleaning agents as many are flammable and/or toxic. Those which are hazardous include:

- paraffin
- white spirit
- carbon tetrachloride
- acids and caustic materials.

Appropriate protective clothing such as gloves, goggles and masks (of the correct type) and barrier cream, together with adequate ventilation, etc. may be needed. **Manufacturers' or suppliers' recommendations and instructions regarding safe practices should be carried out at all times**.

7.b.iii Dyes and markers

These are used to identify individual parts of joints or assemblies. They can also be an aid to the matching of positional locations on re-assembly (Fig. **7**.17). Tags, pen, spray, stencils, electric engraving tools, letter and number stamps (Fig. **7**.18) and centre punches are used.

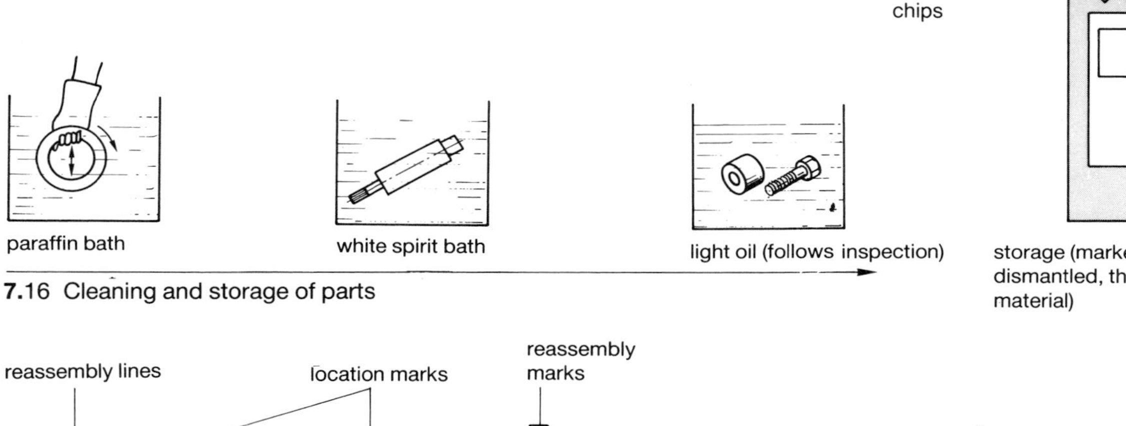

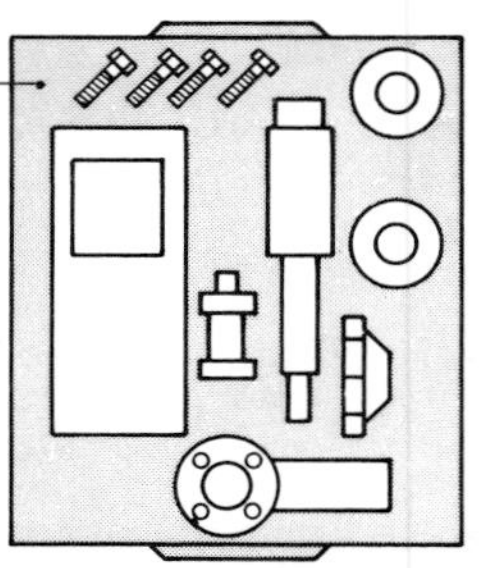

7.16 Cleaning and storage of parts

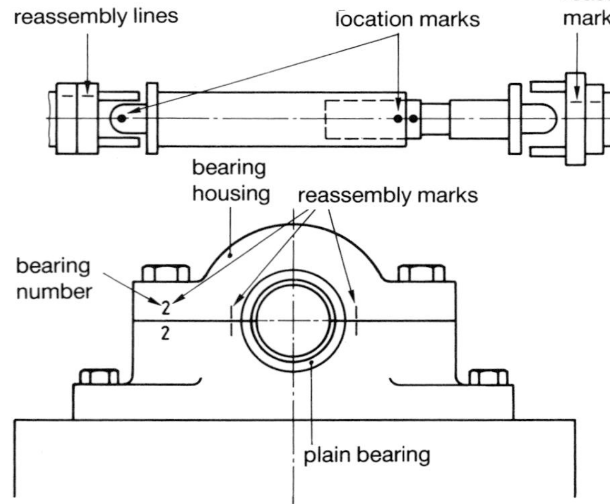

7.17 Location of position marks on assembly

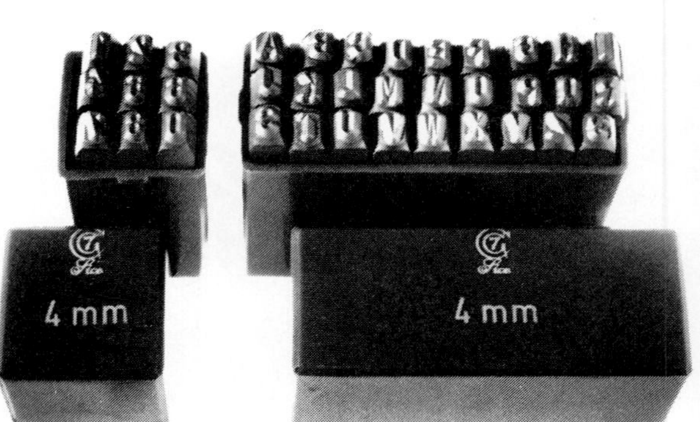

7.18 Number and letter stamps

7.b.iv Penetrating oils

These fluids may assist in the loosening of rusted nuts, bolts, pins, keys and shafts, etc. After the oil has been applied and has penetrated and dissolved the rust, the part can usually be removed.

7.b.v Stud and nut removers; devices for removing broken ends

These are shown in Figs. **7.**19 and **7.**19a shows a stud extractor in position on a stud to be unscrewed. When force is applied, the knurled wheel, being eccentric to the operating shaft, bites into the stud, which is forced to turn in the direction in which the force is applied. Fig. **7.**19b shows a special tool for removing nuts which are otherwise immovable. The teeth of part 2 cut into the nut when part I is tightened, thus splitting the nut.
Fig. **7.**20 shows a screw extractor. The broken screw is filed flat and a hole is drilled into it. The extractor is inserted into the hole and turned with a spanner or tap wrench to release the screw.

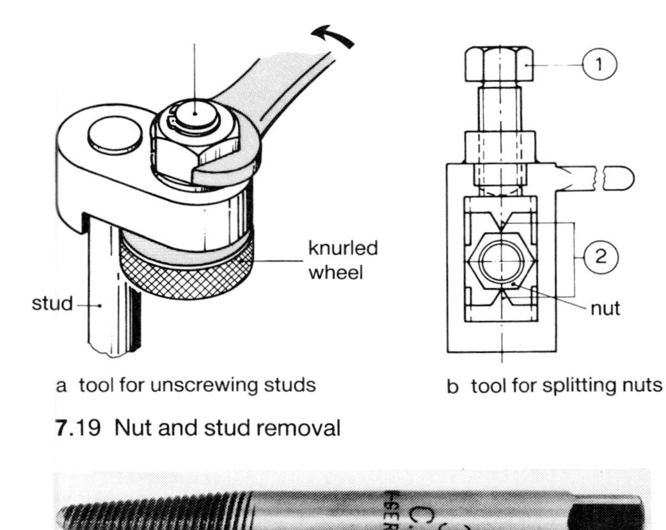

a tool for unscrewing studs b tool for splitting nuts

7.19 Nut and stud removal

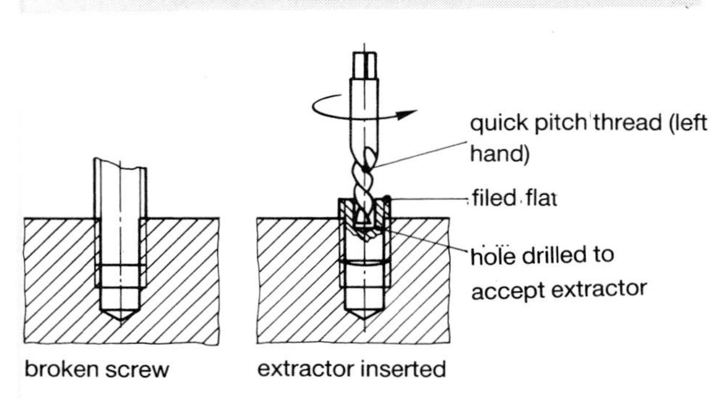

7.20 Tool for removing broken screws and studs

7.b.vi Special purpose spanners and keys

Where special nuts or fastenings have been fitted because of the nature of the operation, adjustment or space, special purpose tools may be required for dismantling. Fig. **7.**21 shows just a small selection; there are many more, e.g. sprung compression tools, etc.

a fuel injection pipe nut spanner

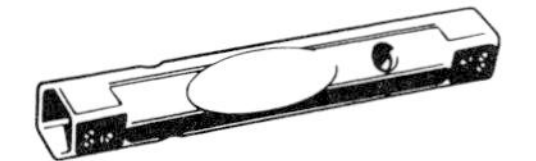

b tubular box spanner

c extra deep socket

d adjustable 'c' hook spanner

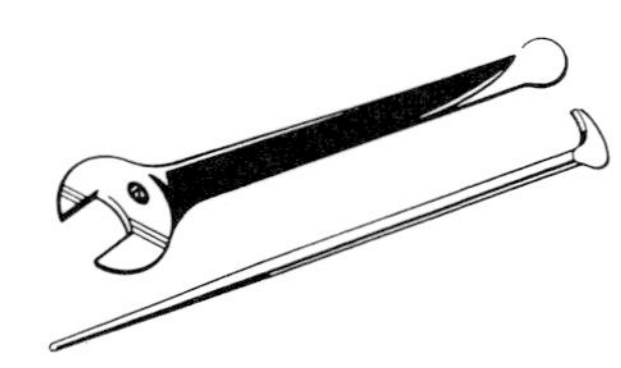

e pry bar and end

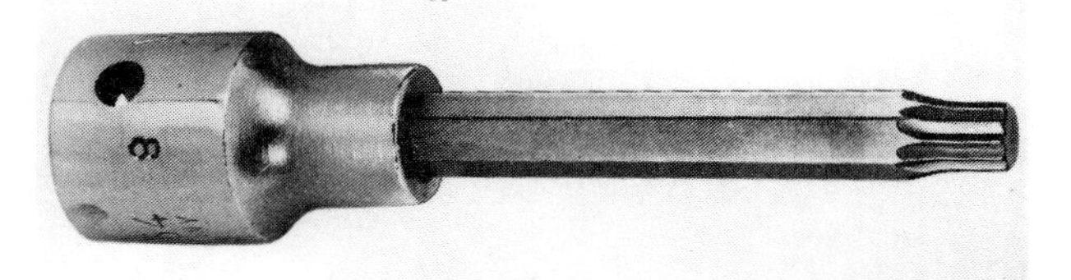

f tool fitting specially shaped bolt and screw heads

7.21 Examples of special tools

7.b.vii Gear pullers

These and devices for removing bearings, flywheels, etc. are shown in Fig. **7.**22a and b; note the even pressure exerted on the inner raceway of the bearing only (arrowed in Fig. **7.**22a).

7.b.viii Presses

The manual and hydraulic presses discussed earlier (Fig. 7.9a and b) are also employed in dismantling, to remove items having interference fits (e.g. bearings, pulleys and wheels).

7.b.ix Heating and flame cutting equipment

This equipment is used where parts cannot be separated by conventional means. This could be a result of severe corrosion, or seizure or inaccessibility of the joint, etc. When heating is used the different expansion rates of the materials cause the joint to split. Fig. 7.23 shows a bearing being cut by oxy-acetylene flame. Note that while in this case the bearing will be unfit for further service, in other circumstances heating can be used without permanent damage to the parts involved. For example, bolts, pulleys and flywheels which have not responded to leverage and penetrating oil may have to be heated to induce separation. Usually such parts are then carefully examined and if found to be undamaged used again.

Safety clothing, goggles, shoes, gloves, must be used when carrying out these operations and safety precautions taken when using the equipment.

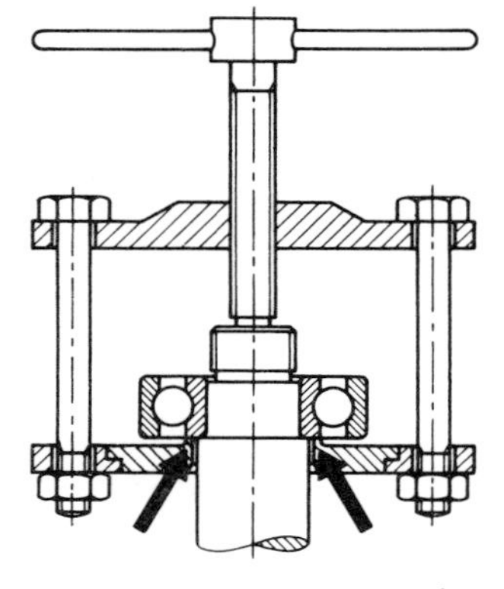

a bearing being removed

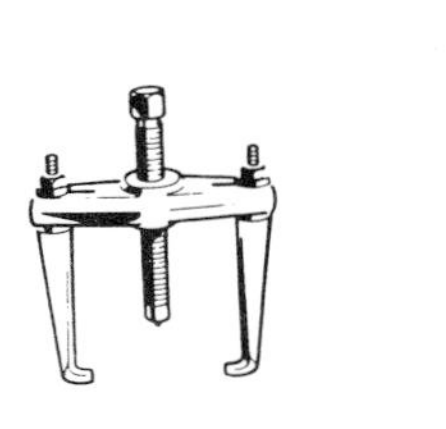

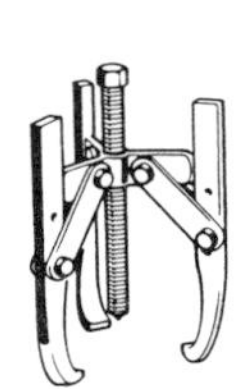

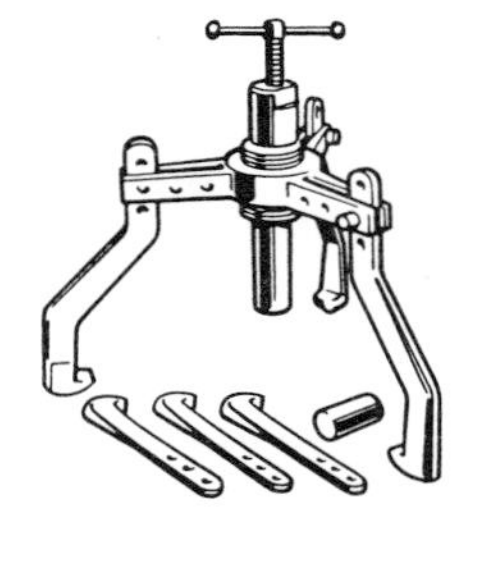

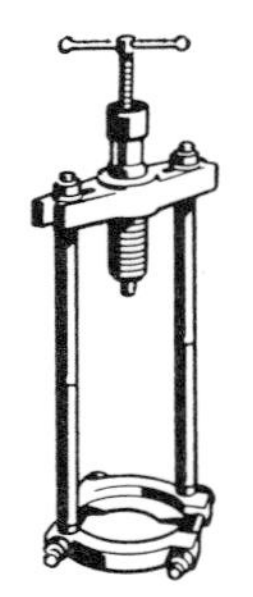

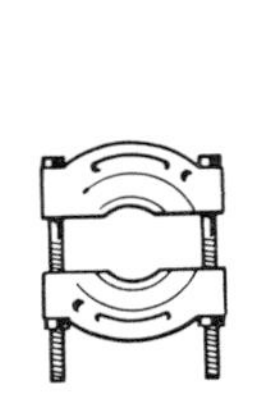

b puller drawer sets

7.22 Gear and bearing pullers

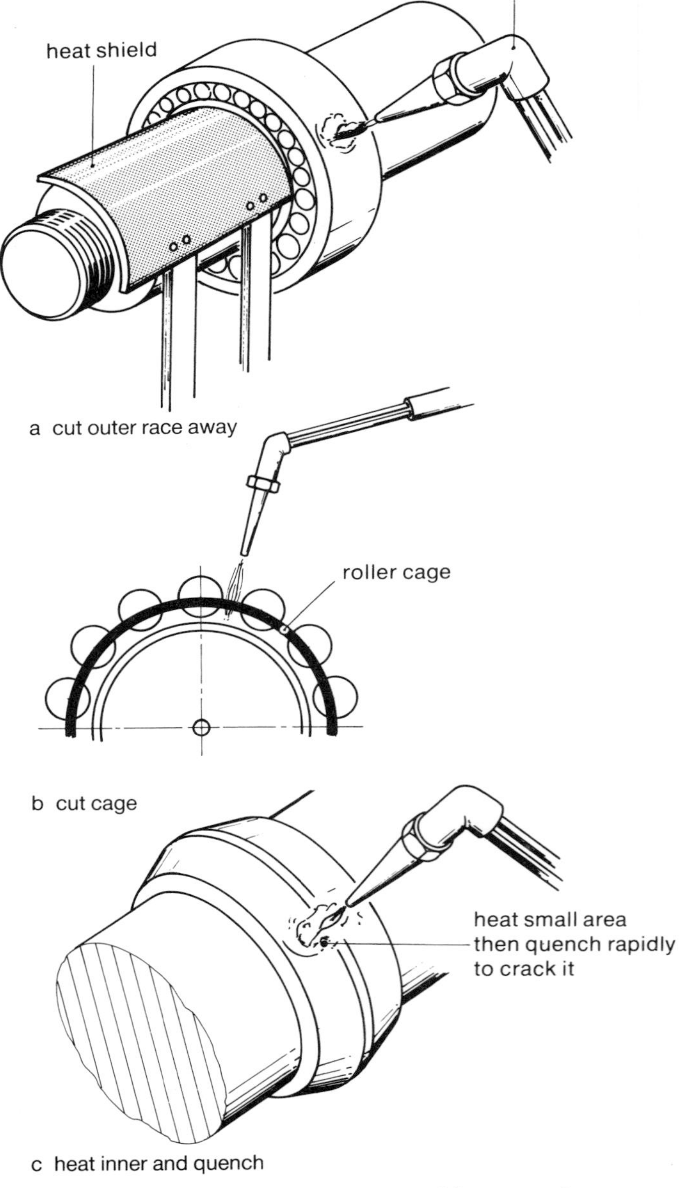

a cut outer race away

b cut cage

c heat inner and quench

7.23 Bearing removal by heating and flame cutting

8 Precautions to be taken

The presence of heavy objects, flammable or noxious fluids, or electricity are only three of the many hazards which may be encountered during assembling or dismantling. A few of the most common hazards and the precautions necessary to deal with them are described in the following text.
Obviously it is impossible to cover all aspects, and nothing can substitute for the sound practical training and supervised experience needed to develop a safe approach when such hazards are present.

8.a Examples of acting forces

Some examples are given here. More detailed information can be obtained by reference to the series book *Observing Safe Practices and Moving Loads*.

- The mass of the parts themselves: heavy objects which are subject to distortion must be correctly supported during dismantling, transport and storage. Fig. **8.**1 shows a heavy machine table being lifted and stored. Possible distortion of the bed could occur if it was lifted or supported at other points, such as the ends or centre.
- The liquid contents of partially filled containers tend to move and the centre of gravity changes at the same time (Fig. **8.**2a and b). Correct positioning of the lifting slings would make this operation safe (Fig. **8.**2c).
  The applied load must always be lower than the safe working load.

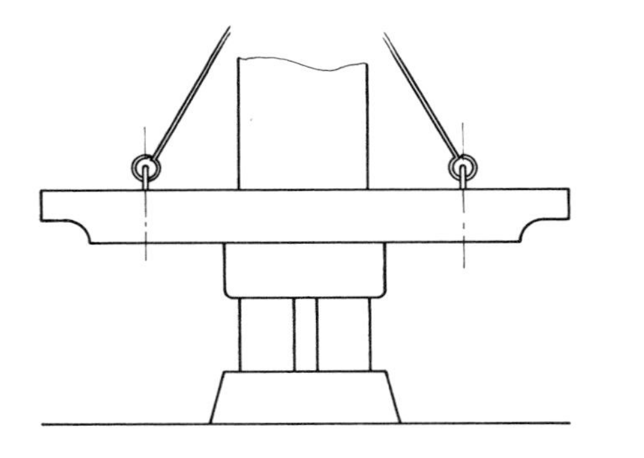

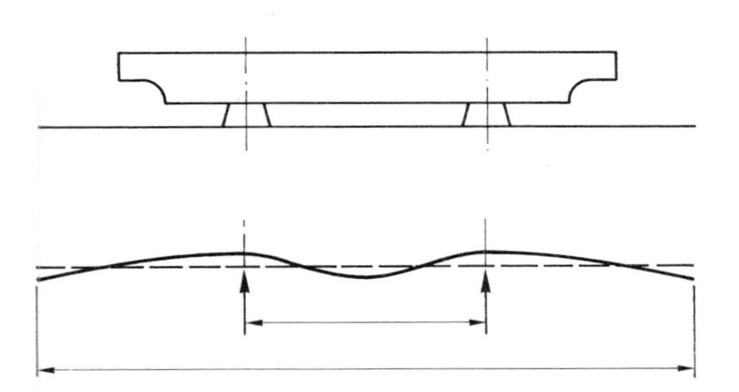

8.1 Lifting and storing a machine table at points of minimum deflection (Airey Points)

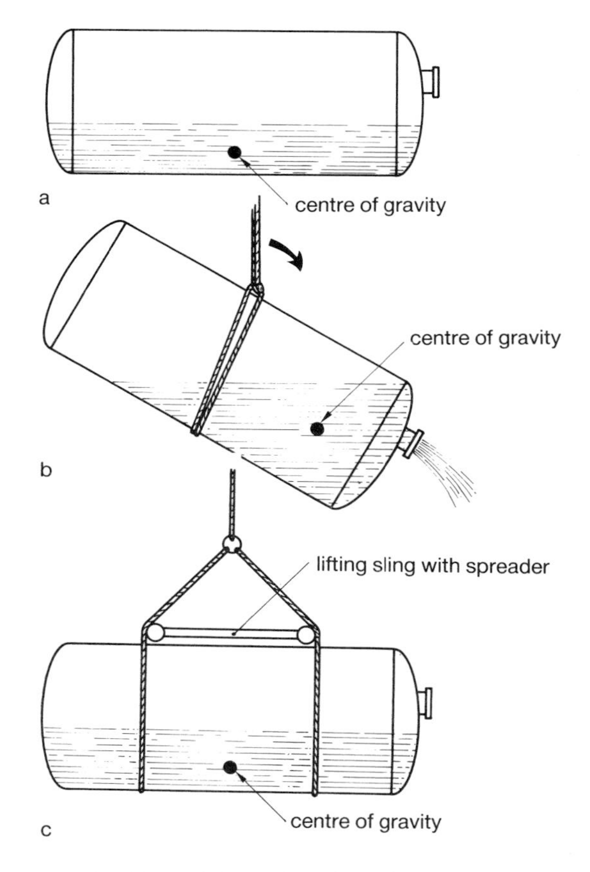

8.2 Shifting of the point of gravity

8.b Pressure or flammability of system contents or components

Before dismantling, measures must be taken so that:

- the part to be dismantled is not under pressure, i.e. the appropriate valves have been operated to release any pressure present
- no pressure can be released or introduced by someone else. e.g. by attachment of blank flanges (Fig. **8**.3). locking off valves and the placing of warning notices (Fig. **8**.4).
- ignition and explosion of flammable matter or gases are prevented. Fire and naked light must be forbidden. Sparkless tools may be necessary. Hazard and warning notices must be displayed.

'Permit to work' procedures (Fig. **8**.5) must be observed and if need be, reference made to BS 1710 colour coding for pipe contents, to identify the system contents, pressure and temperature (Fig. **8**.6). See Chapter 8 of the series book entitled *Interpreting Drawings, Specifications and Data* for further information on colour coding.

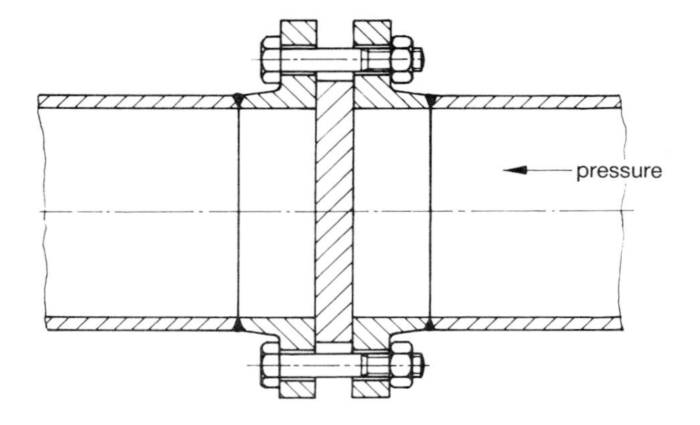

8.3 A blank flange

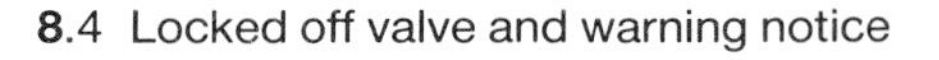

8.4 Locked off valve and warning notice

A Permit-to-Work authorising the performance of maintenance work on a refrigeration plant might include:

(1) Period of validity from ________ hrs to ________ hrs on ________

(2) Issuing authority ________

(3) Identification of plant to be worked on ________

(4) Description of work ________

(5) Safety action to be taken:

(a) Electrical supplies isolated   Signature ________

(b) Cold storage permission   Signature ________

(c) Refrigeration system isolated   Signature ________

(d) Refrigeration system 'gas freed'   Signature ________

(6) Acceptance
I certify that I understand the above instructions and that this permit is valid unless all safety actions have been completed and certified.

Time ________ Date ________ Signature ________

(7) Completion of work
I certify that the work for which this permit was issued has been completed and that the equipment is fit for return to service.

Time ________ Date ________ Signature ________

8.5 Example of a permit to work form (part of)

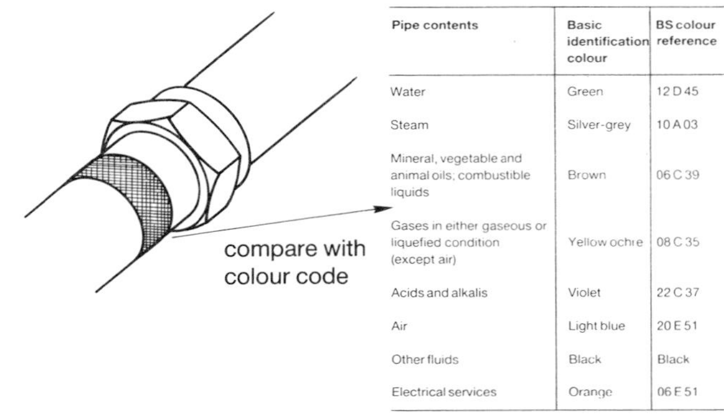

Pipe contents	Basic identification colour	BS colour reference
Water	Green	12 D 45
Steam	Silver-grey	10 A 03
Mineral, vegetable and animal oils; combustible liquids	Brown	06 C 39
Gases in either gaseous or liquefied condition (except air)	Yellow ochre	08 C 35
Acids and alkalis	Violet	22 C 37
Air	Light blue	20 E 51
Other fluids	Black	Black
Electrical services	Orange	06 E 51

8.6 For colour coding of pipes refer to BS 1710

8.c Electricity

Assembling and dismantling machines and constructions either driven by electric motors or switched by electrical apparatus such as relays, can be dangerous. Under present electrical regulations only trained and competent persons may work on live circuits or live exposed parts, on high voltage work or jobs requiring permits to work. This limitation of who may connect or disconnect electrical conductors extends to the removal and replacement of fuses.

It is within that understanding of the situation that the following precautions are stated as necessary:

- The possibility of contact with electricity during assembly and dismantling must be eliminated (Fig. **8**.7a). Fig. **8**.7b shows the supply locked on. In this case it may be dangerous to turn the supply off and therefore it is important to follow any standing instructions covering the situation or to check with an appropriate person.
- Ensure that it is impossible for anyone to connect electricity to the machine during assembly or dismantling. This may entail removal of fuses or the locking-off of switches, as shown in Fig. **8.**8. In this example three people must check that the situation is safe for the supply to be restored.

8.d Temperature

When dismantling pumps, machines, compressors and pipe lines from systems containing hot gases and/or liquids, precautions must be taken to prevent the hot substances escaping. The installation of blank flanges will be necessary in such cases (Fig. **8.**3).

8.7a Electrical supply locked 'off'

8.7b Electrical supply locked 'on'

8.8 Example of locked-off switch requiring three persons to check installation before turning supply 'on'

8.e Chemicals

When work is carried out in an installation featuring dangerous chemicals, any particular section involved in the work must be shut off and the possibility of its being reactivated must be eliminated.
Rules of procedure must be laid down within the organisation operating the plant. There may also be overriding regulations or requirements prescribed by state or the Government Inspectorate. All relevant rules and regulations must be strictly followed.

The safety precautions necessary for this section fall into three main types.

- 'Permit to work' procedures; these are detailed procedures which include the issue of a written authority to carry out the work signed by an authorised person (Fig. **8**.5). This person will ensure that all safety precautions and necessary actions are taken, will enter on the permit what may be done by whom and what equipment is safe.
- 'Locking-off' procedures; Figs. **8**.4, **8**.7 and **8**.8 show the nature of these.
- Emptying and 'purging' procedures; these are used for effectively discharging and neutralising the dangerous contents (including gases) within those parts of a system to be opened or entered (more about this will be found in Section 12, which deals with dismantling pipework).

8.f Radiation

Another source of danger arises from radiation. Light (e.g. lasers), radioactivity, microwaves and X rays are all possible sources of harmful radiation which may be present in workplaces where assembling and dismantling are carried out. Precautions to guard against exposure, which may not produce any immediate sensation, will vary according to the nature of the radiation.

- Light: suitable clothing and goggles provide protection
- Radioactivity: do not approach closer than the warning signs permit and do not handle any radioactive source (Fig. **8**.9)
- Microwaves: suitable screening provides protection
- X rays: warning signs will be displayed and precautions will be taken in accordance with both nationally and locally approved procedures and instructions.

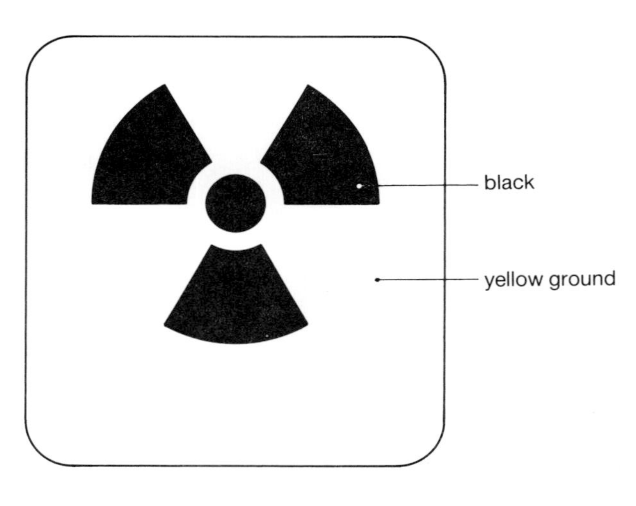

8.9 Radiation hazard warning sign

9 The effect of material properties on assembling and dismantling

In the assembling and dismantling processes regard must be paid to the properties of materials used for the following:

- joining devices
- the components
- sealing agents and devices.

We shall examine the more important aspects of these and also some ways in which corrosion and its prevention may influence assembling and dismantling.

9.a Material properties of joining devices

Fig. **9**.1 shows the tensile curves of bolt materials having tensile strengths of 360, 590, and 780 N/mm^2 respectively. The ratio of the diameters of two bolts of equal strength is shown in Fig. **9**.2. Again two bolts of equal strength are shown in Fig. **9**.3. The socket head bolt is made of a material with a higher tensile strength than is the hexagon head bolt; the socket head bolt can therefore be smaller, but still retain the same strength as the hexagon bolt.

In addition to the material from which bolts are made, the manufacturing method is also of great importance. Drop forged bolts with rolled threads are stronger than machined bolts of the same material (Figs. **9**.4 to **9**.6). In these figures the grain lines are illustrated. Grain lines can be likened to the grain in wood; it is easier to cut with, or down the grain than to cut across it. Fig. **9**.7 shows applications where tensile strength is of great importance. It should be noted that where special materials are used for such parts as rivets, screws, nuts and bolts, they are usually identified by marking (Fig. **9**.4c) or colour coding. During replacement it is important that the same marked component is inserted in the assembly. If it is available, the specification should be consulted for confirmation of the correct grade and marking.

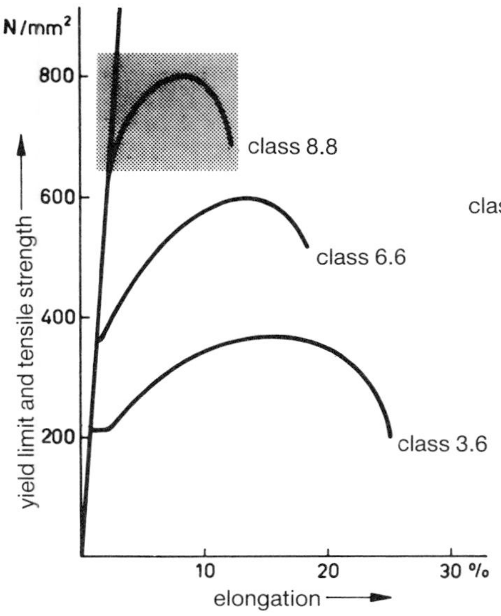

9.1 Tensile curves of bolt materials

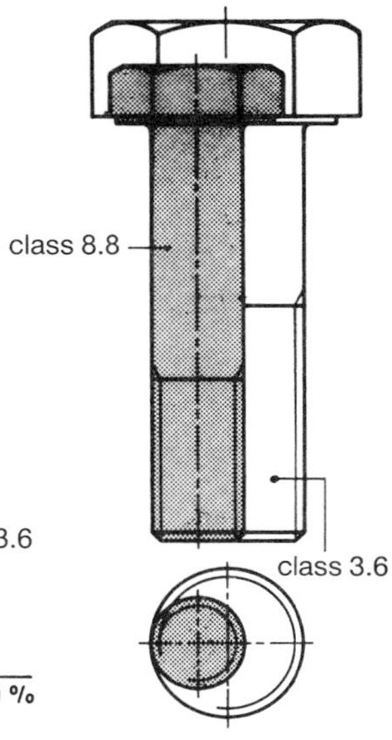

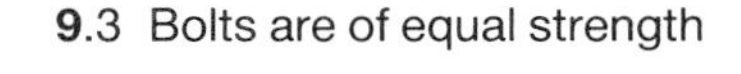

9.2 Bolts are of equal strength

9.3 Bolts are of equal strength

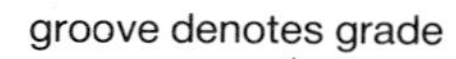

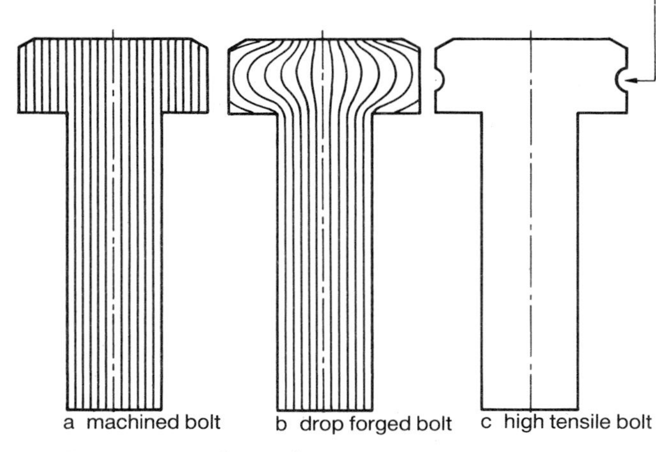

9.4 Bolts – types of manufacture

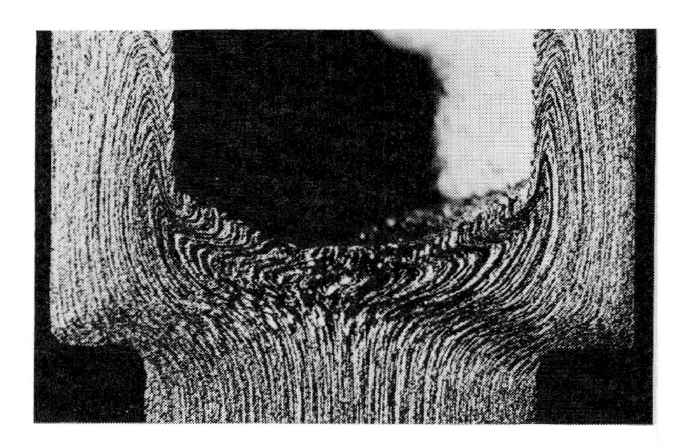

9.5 Drop forged hexagon socket cap head bolt

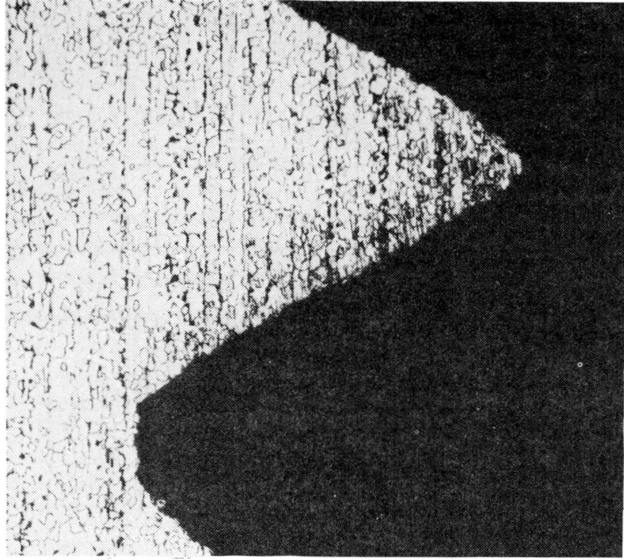

a machined (cut) thread

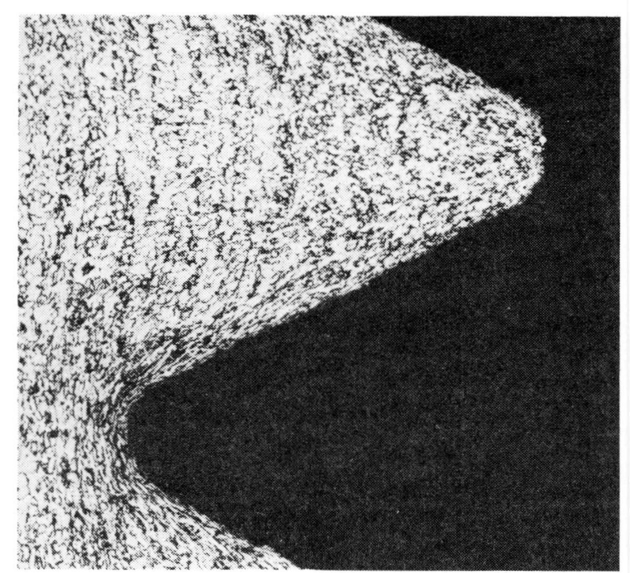

b rolled screw thread

9.6 Screw thread – manufacturing process

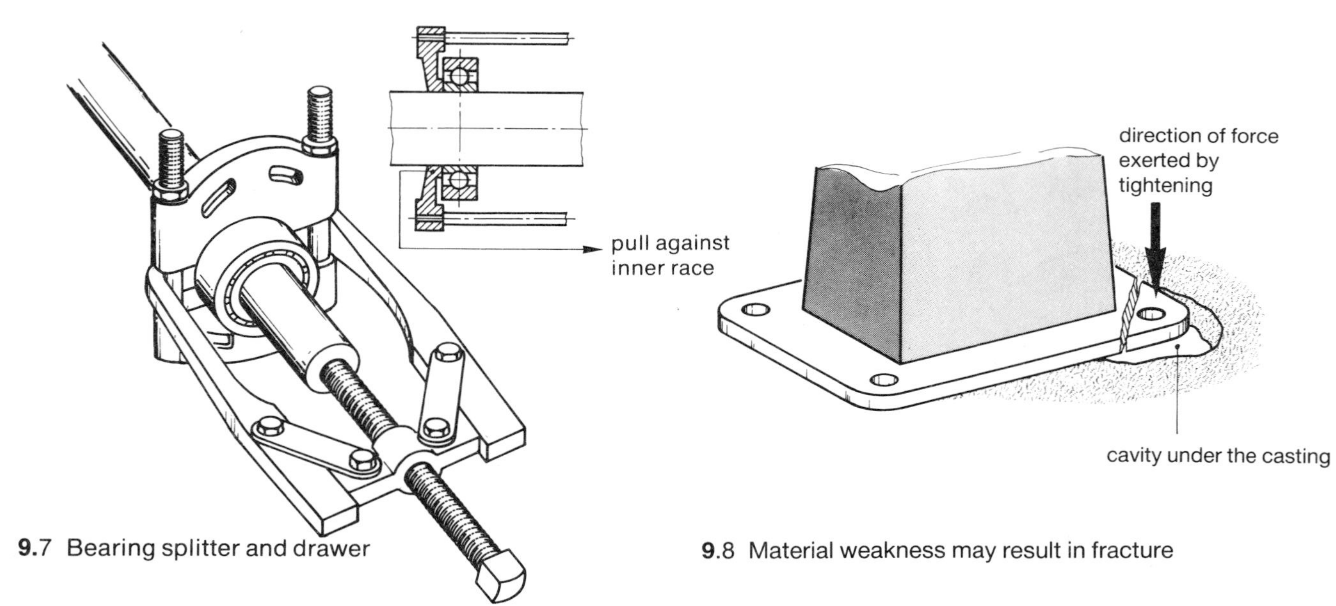

9.7 Bearing splitter and drawer

9.8 Material weakness may result in fracture

9.b Material properties in components

- *Weakness in tensile and shear strength:* When the cast iron base of a centrifugal pump bears on three faces instead of four, the base is liable to break suddenly when the bolts are tightened (Fig. **9.**8). Materials weak in tension and shear must be adequately supported to prevent breakage.
- *Brittleness:* When bearings or cast iron pulleys are assembled or dismantled by using drifts or 'dollies' and hammers, soft materials should be used for the drifts or dollies; otherwise splinters of metal and even breakage or damage to the part may occur. This is because materials like hardened steel and cast iron are brittle and are likely to break under shock loads (Fig. **9.**9).

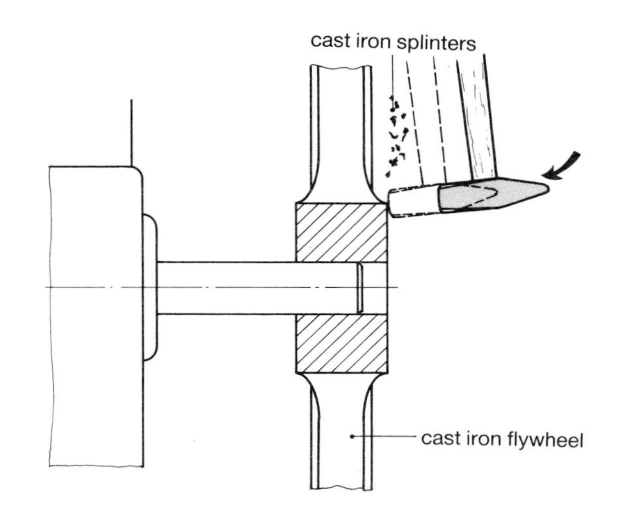

9.9 Compressor flywheel assembly

9.c Materials for sealing devices

When a choice has to be made of pipe flange packing, shape, dimensions and the following factors will determine the type and quality of the material to be used:

- the nature of the fluid flowing through the pipes
- the temperature of the content
- the pressure.

Flange packing materials such as cork and rubber are adequate for sealing joints retaining some liquids including water, when at low temperature and pressure. However, higher temperatures and pressures and the presence of some chemicals may require the use of asbestos, bronze, copper, synthetic materials or a combination of such materials.

Note: Asbestos is a toxic material. On no account should attempts be made to machine or file it outside a controlled environment.

9.d Corrosion and its prevention

- The attacking of metal by the atmosphere, water and other matter is called corrosion. Designers need to choose materials and finishes best suited to the known working environment. Thus, parts which cannot be provided with a protective layer after assembly, must be treated for corrosion prevention before assembly (Fig. **9.**10). It is equally important that replacements are to the original specification or receive similar treatment.

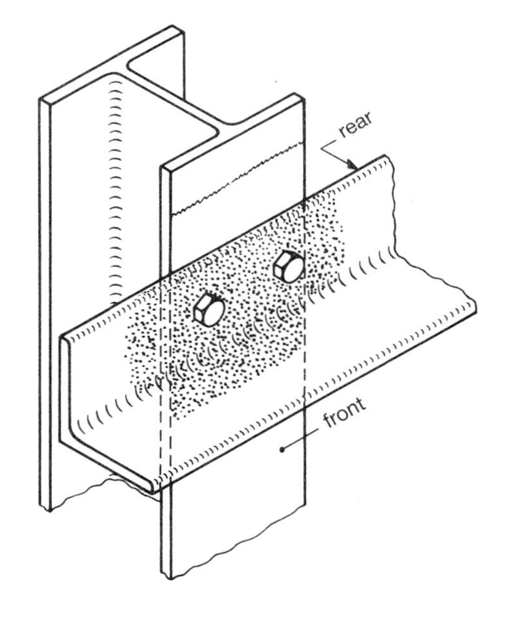

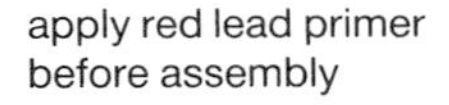

9.10 Treatment to prevent corrosion

- Corrosion by contact; when metals are joined together and the joint is exposed to the atmosphere or water, a galvanic cell is formed. Fig. **9.**11a shows this type of galvanic cell where zinc is locally corroding on contact with copper. This phenomenon can be prevented by using similar materials for fasteners or by isolating the fasteners from the component parts (Fig. **9.**11b-c).
- Anti-corrosive treatments are usually specified on drawings of the parts concerned.

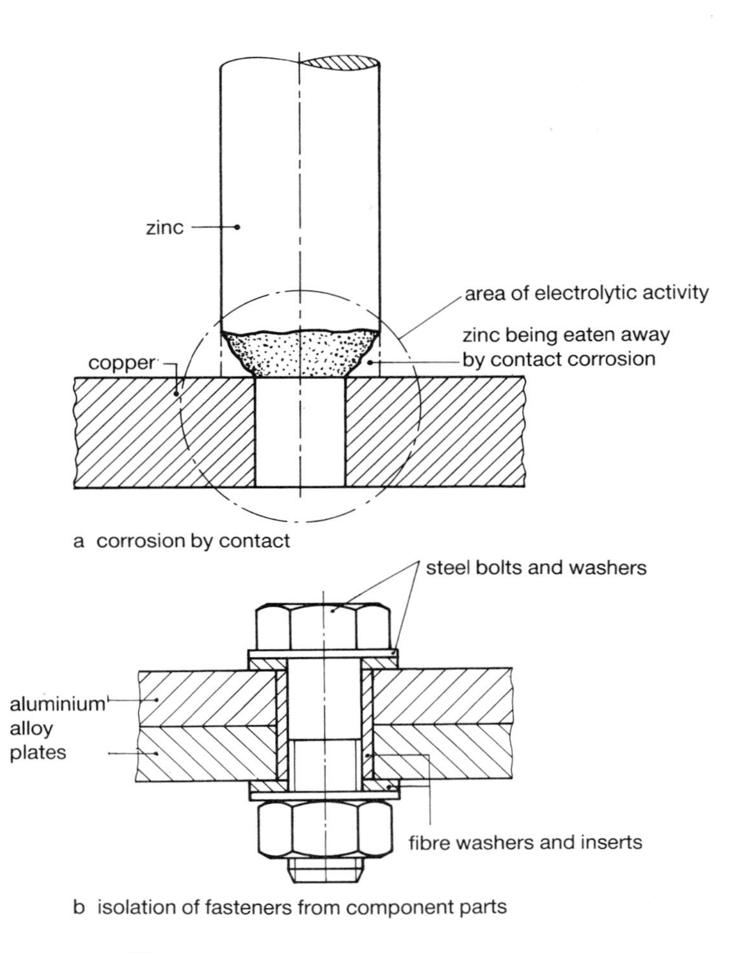

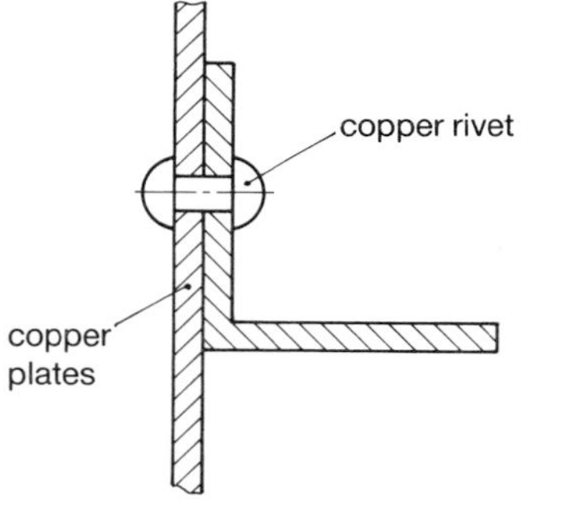

9.11 Illustration of how corrosion by contact occurs and two methods of combating it

10 General rules for assembling and dismantling

These rules for assembling and dismantling are summarised separately. Some rules are common to both operations and for the sake of completeness they are repeated.

10.a Assembly

10.a.i-viii The key aspects of assembly

- *assembly drawings and specifications:* if available these must be carefully scrutinised and all relevant points observed, e.g. the use of correct materials, fits, joints, locking devices, etc.
- *assembly sequence:* this should comply with specifications. If these are not available, the sequence should be planned before assembly.
- *parts and tools:* all necessary items should be available and be in a clean condition.
- *sealing:* penetration of dirt and other undesirable matter must be prevented (Fig. **10**.1a and b).
- *joints:* correctly fitted fasteners of specified quality must be used for all joints.
- *use of tools:* tightening tools must fit correctly (Figs. **10**.2 and **10**.3) and the correct torque must be applied.
- *identification and tightening:* parts must be assembled in accordance with any location markings on them (Fig. **10**.5), using the correct tightening sequence (Fig. **10**.4).

a

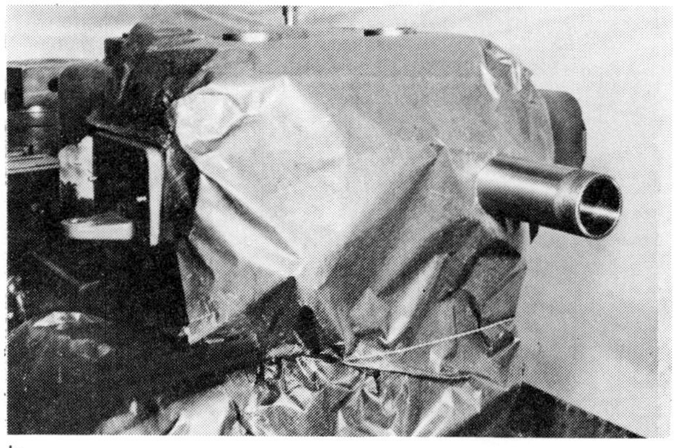

b

10.1 Protection with waxed paper or clean nap-free cloth

10.2 Correctly fitting tools (screwdriver)

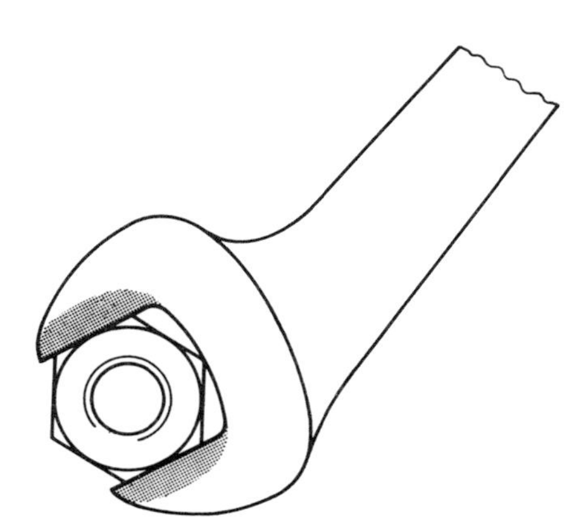

10.3 Correctly fitting tools (spanner)

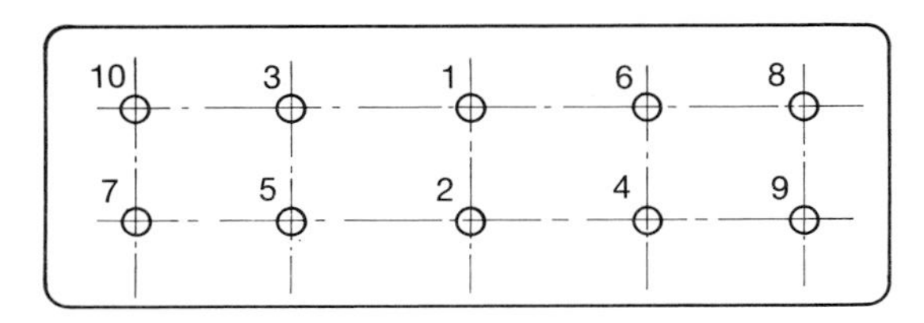

10.4 Sequence of tightening engine cylinder head bolts

10.5 Assembly marks – balance shaft, camshaft and crankshaft

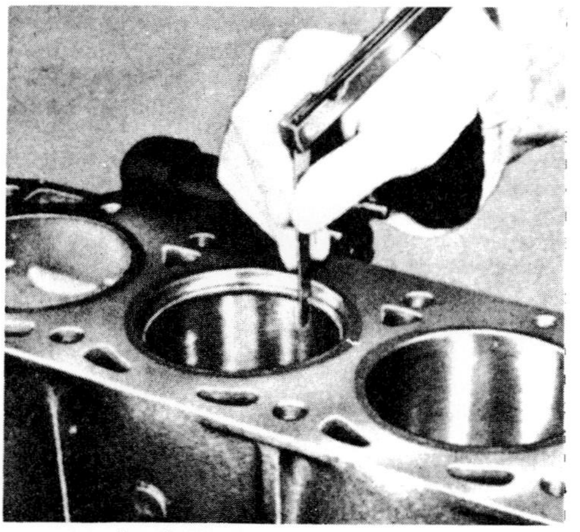

a measuring the gap

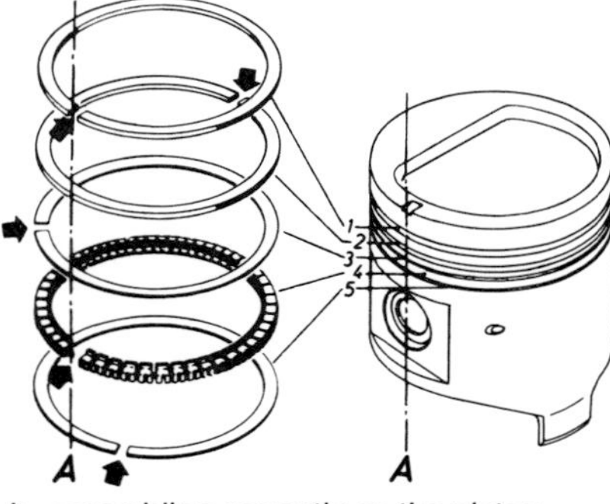

b assembling correctly on the piston

10.7 Piston ring assembly

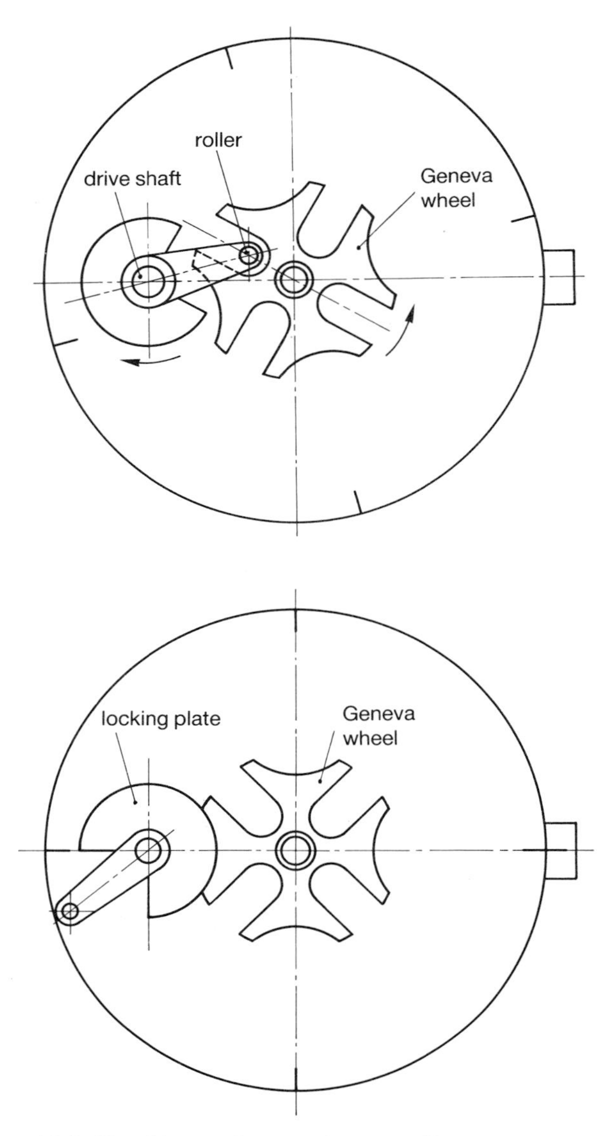

10.6 Checking and measuring operation

10.a.ix Inspection

Inspection, checking and measuring must be done in sequence as the work proceeds and permits. Checking should include:

- dimensional accuracy (Fig. **7**.10)
- correct position (Fig. **7**.11)
- clearances (Fig. **7**.13)
- concentricity (Fig. **7**.14)
- operation (Fig. **10**.6)

Example 1: piston ring assembly (Fig. **10**.7).

Example 2: operation of a rotary table can be checked when the assembly has reached the appropriate stage by carefully rotating the drive-shaft. If correctly assembled the table will rotate only through 90° every one revolution of the drive-shaft when the roller is engaged with the Geneva wheel. The locking plate positively locks the table in position until the drive-shaft is rotated sufficiently (another 270°) to engage roller and Geneva wheel (Fig. **10**.6). Note the setting marks on the table.

Example 3: to establish the correct functioning of the headstock of a lathe, apply a cutting test. If micrometer readings taken at A and B differ (Fig. **10**.8) after a light cut has been taken errors may be present in alignment, levelling or both.

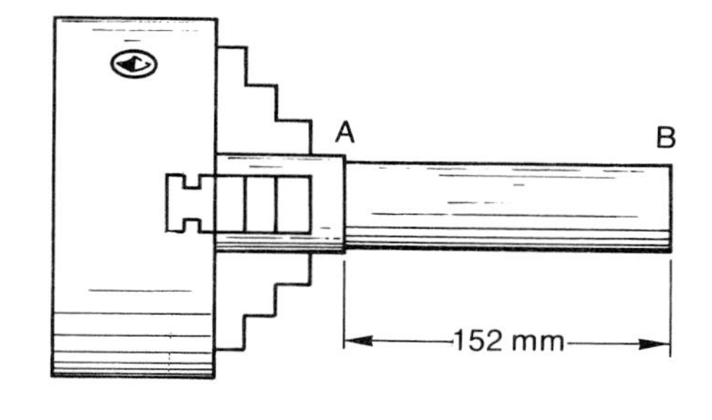

10.8 Checking a lathe headstock (micrometer readings at A and B)

10.a.x Safety

Safety procedures must be strictly observed when any assembling work is undertaken.

10.b Dismantling

10.b.i Drawings and specifications

Assembly drawings and specifications, if available, must be carefully checked for relevant information e.g. the types of materials, joints, fits, locking devices etc. used. (Operation of the assembly and its component parts must be understood.)

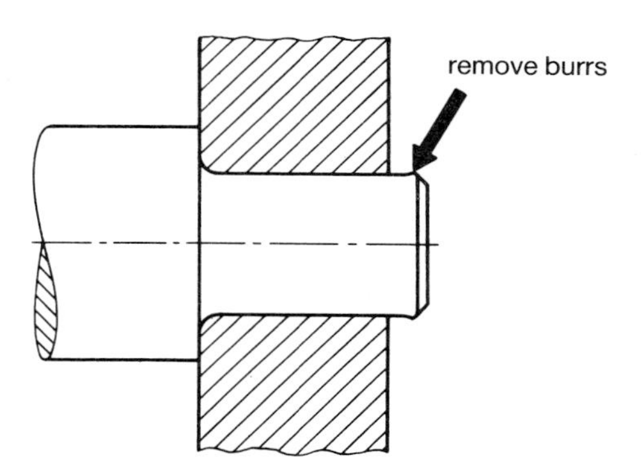

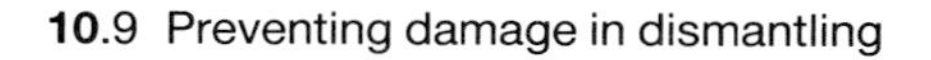

10.9 Preventing damage in dismantling

10.b.ii Sequence of operations

The dismantling sequence should comply with specifications. If these are not available the sequence should be planned before the start of dismantling.

10.b.iii Parts and tools

The correct tools and equipment should be selected.

10.b.iv Burrs and corrosion

Imperfections (burrs, rust) must be removed. They may cause damage or difficulties in dismantling (Figs. **10**.9 and **10**.10).

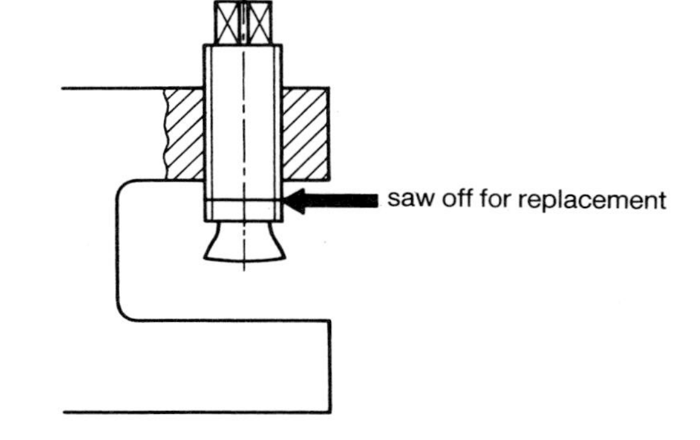

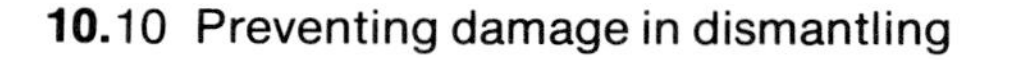

10.10 Preventing damage in dismantling

10.b.v Tools

Causing damage to components must be avoided at all times. Soft metal drifts, soft hammers, etc. should be used where applicable (Fig. **10.**11). Pullers and levers must be used with care.

10.b.vi Use of lubricants and extractors

In many cases oil applied to threads, shafts, key-ways, etc. will make dismantling easier. Threaded holes for extractor screws and other provisions will also aid dismantling (Figs. **10.**12 and **10.**13).

10.b.vii Identification of position

Marking the position and relationship of the various components, especially matching parts, must be done in accordance with the sequence in which the components are dismantled (Fig. **10.**14).

10.b.viii Inspection

Observe signs of excessive wear, corrosion by chemicals, etc. The onset or presence of excessive wear can be recognised by:

- oil contaminated by metallic particles
- rough, grooved or discoloured bearing surfaces (Figs. **10.**15 and **10.**16)
- excessive play (Fig. **10.**17).

Parts fitted to close limits (e.g. journal bearings) will need to be measured with precision instruments and the dimensions should be compared with the maker's specified limits.

10.b.ix Care of components

Measures should be taken to prevent penetration of dirt into cleaned components (Fig. **10.**18) and any damage during storage, including that to working surfaces and that which might arise from distortion.

10.b.x Safety

Safety rules must be strictly observed and all dismantling should proceed to a safe system of work, e.g. using 'Permits to Work', locking-off procedures and special care in lifting.

10.11 Using a soft metal drift

10.12 Using a set screw to extract a bearing

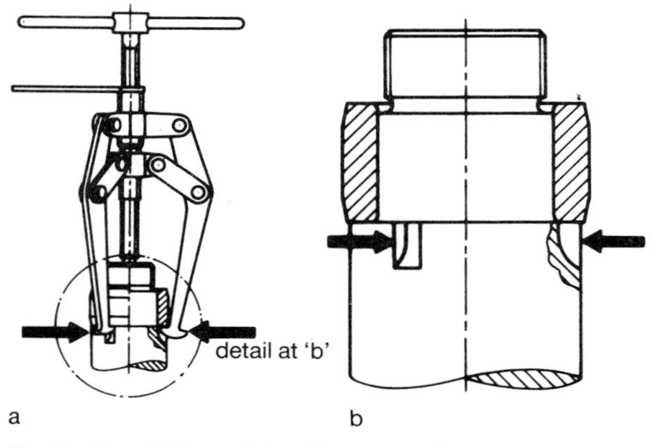

10.13 Special provision for extraction

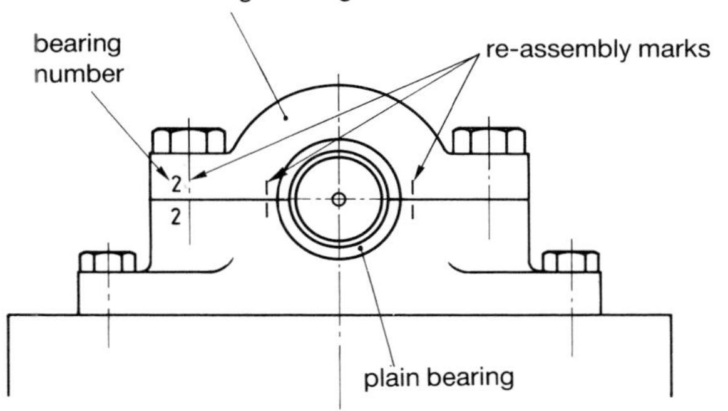

10.14 Position and relationship marks

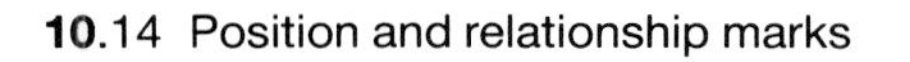

10.15 Outer race discoloured and pitted

10.16 Races grooved and pitted

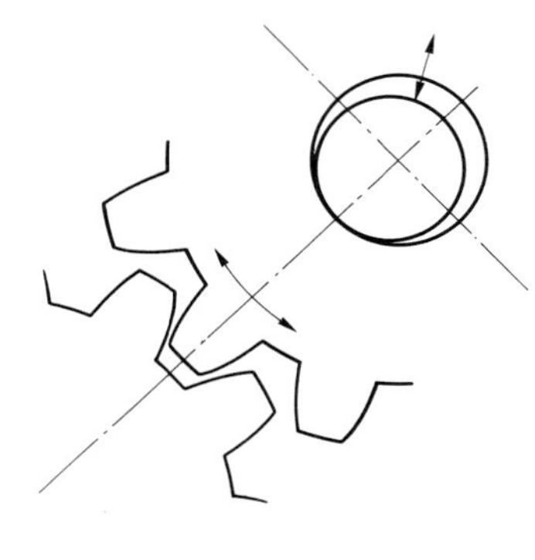

10.17 Evidence of excessive play

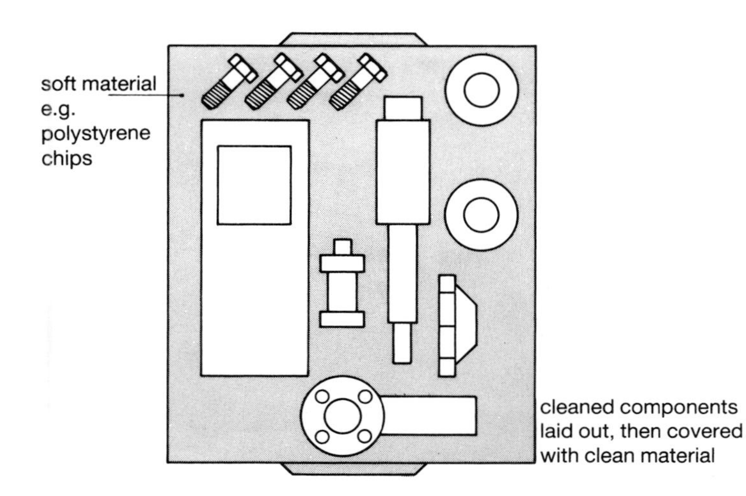

10.18 Storage of cleaned components

11 Pipework systems

The contents of a pipe will be a major factor in deciding the sort of pipe to be used in any system. So we must look at how pipes vary according to their application and shall go on to consider how this affects assembly work.

11.a The application of pipes to pipework systems

The many applications for which pipes are used include: gas pipes, water pipes, effluent pipes, oil pipes and steam pipes. There are also pipes for conveying liquid and gaseous chemical products and powders.

Pipes used to convey factory service fluids such as water, steam or gas usually work at low to medium pressures and temperatures. Seamed steel tube can accommodate these conditions and is relatively cheap. Where higher pressures for transmission of fluid power are needed, e.g. hydraulic systems, a stronger pipe or tube is required and is more expensive to produce. High pressure steam also needs this stronger pipe. Fig. **11**.1 shows the two basic constructions.

11.a.i Seam jointed: 8 to 150 mm diameter

This pipe (Fig. **11**.1a) is made in three grades using light, medium and heavy gauge steel. Applications include the conveying of water, steam, petrol and gas. Medium or heavy grades must be selected when the contents are gas. The standard joint specified in BS 1387 is parallel, screwed and socketed. This is widely used for suitable services at low or moderate pressures. It is not considered practical to lay down precise limits for working pressures as the joint's effectiveness is very dependent on size, local service and support conditions and jointing techniques. Therefore, maximum design pressures for heavy gauge pipe may vary between 8 and 17 bar for 150 mm diameter and 21 to 42 bar for 8 mm diameter pipe.

11.a.ii Seamless (no joint)

Seamless pipe (Fig. **11**.1b) is usually referred to as tube. The materials from which it is made and the thickness of the tube wall are determined by the nature and pressure of the contents. **Table 11**.1 gives an indication of the sizes available in various materials, the related working pressures and uses.

Note that the sizes given are the average largest and smallest, but that larger tubes are available in nearly all materials on special request to the manufacturers.

11.a.iii Plastic pipes

These are suitable for carrrying chemicals such as acids and alkalis. Plastic or rubber pipes are often used to line a stronger pipe, e.g. steel, where protection and strength are both required. When plastic pipe is used, operating temperature has to be carefully considered; if it is too high the plastic may deform.

Fig. **11**.2 shows a flexible pipe combining synthetic rubber and high tensile steel that is designed to be used at between − 40°C to + 135°C at pressures from 43 to 207 bar.

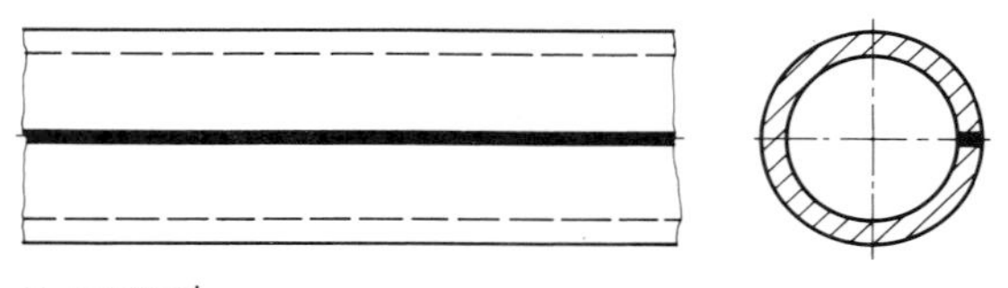

a seamed

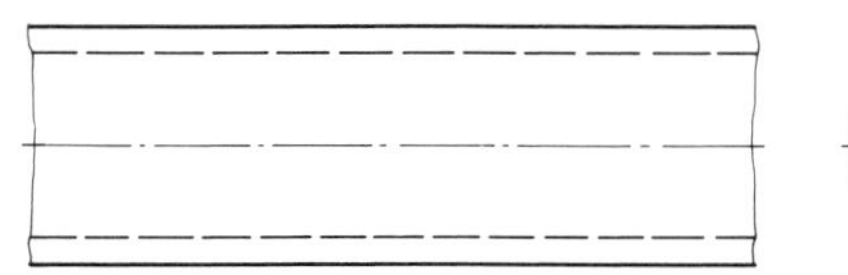
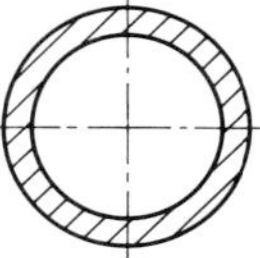

b seamless

11.1 The basic construction of pipes

11.2 Braided hose

Table 11.1 Seamless tube materials, sizes, uses and pressures

Material	Diameter mm	Pressure bar	Uses
Steel	6-42	633-151	High pressure fluids such as hydraulic oil and high pressure steam.
Cast iron	80-300 300-1600	40 25	Low pressure fluids such as gas, water or oil drainage lines, although it is used for steam and water main lines at higher pressures.
Copper (soft)	4-12	128-64	Medium pressure fluids such as compressed air, hydraulic oil, and water.
Copper (½ hard)	4-28	340-90	As above but higher pressures may be used.
Plastics	4-28	26-15	Widely used on small diameter pneumatic, low pressure hydraulic and water systems.
Plastics	28 plus		Large capacity feed and drain systems such as cooling lines.

Use the above table only as a guide.
Example: a steel pipe of 6 mm diameter will withstand 633 bar pressure and can be used for high pressure steam or hydraulics.

11.b Assembling pipework

Pressure, temperature and the purpose for which pipes are used determine the method of assembly. In assembling pipes for liquids and gases, a distinction can be made between:

- 'in line' connections (Figs. **11.3**-**11.6**).
- connecting pipes to system components such as pumps and valves (Fig. **11**.7a, b and c).
- making branch connections (Figs. **11.8**-**11.10**).

Usually a combination of these operations is involved when assembling a pipework system.

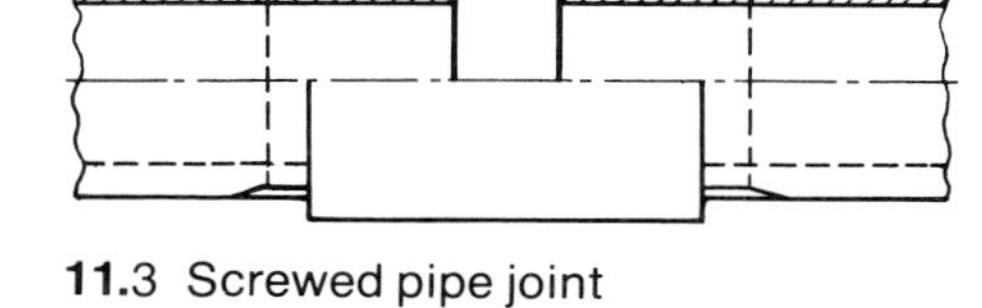

11.3 Screwed pipe joint

11.4 Welded pipe joint

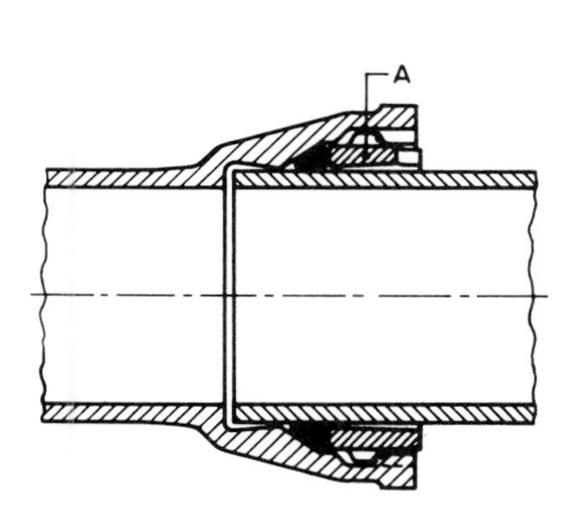

11.5 Sleeved joint

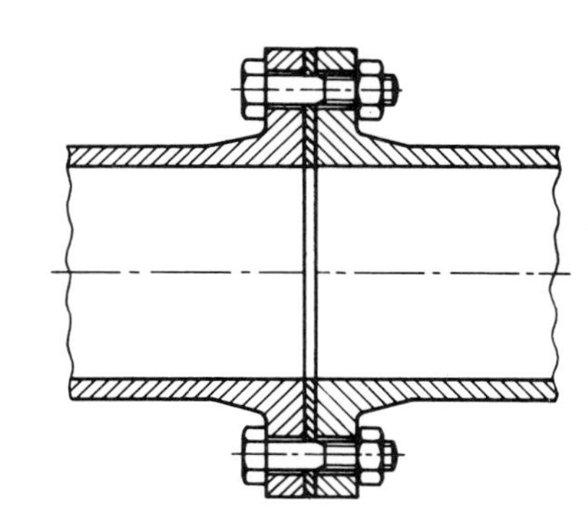

11.6 Flange joint

tilt cylinder
lift cylinder
overflow hose
lift control lever
tilt control lever
tilt cylinder
tank
constant volume pump
directional control valve

a typical system diagram – forklift truck, as in (b) below

b forklift truck

c flange joints to pumps, valves and pipes

11.7 Use of pipes and valves in hydraulic engineering

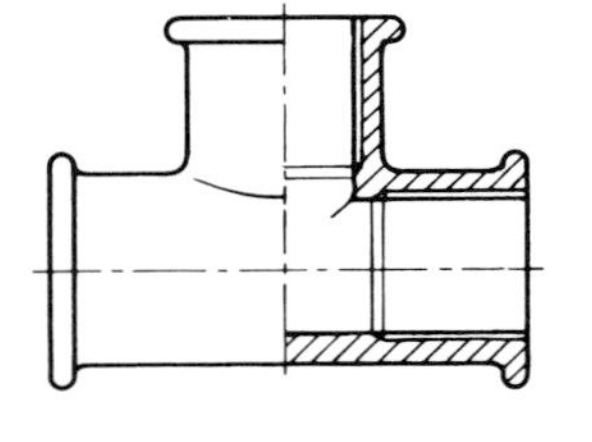

11.8 Screwed T branch piece

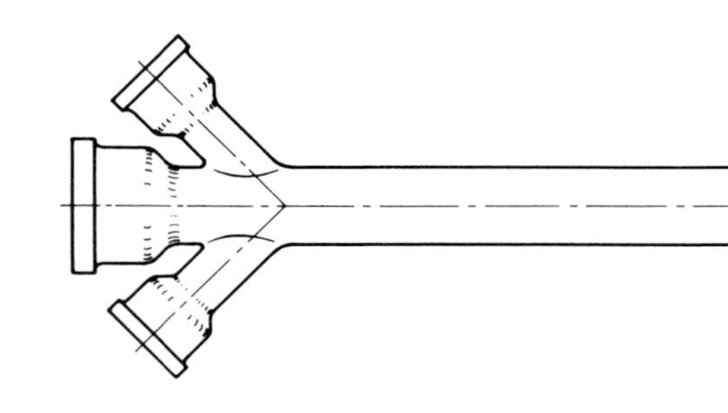

11.9 Double- end branch piece

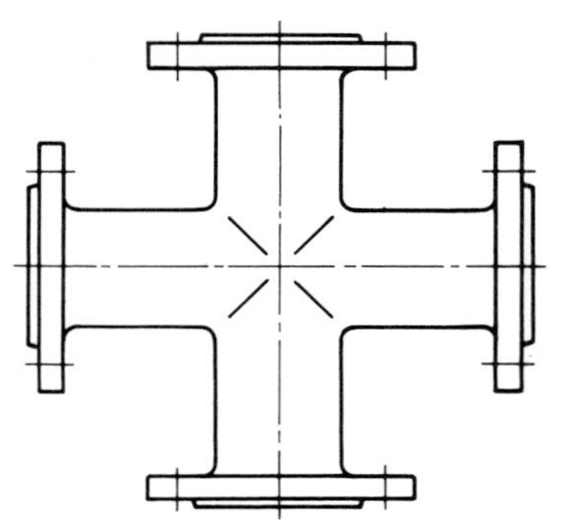

11.10 Flange cross branch piece

11.c Pipe joints

Methods commonly used to join pipes are listed below:

- pipe fittings with screwed threads are made from steel, malleable iron and brass and are used to join steel pipes
- sleeved joints can be used to join metal and plastic pipes. The sealing of the joint is achieved by using rubber, lead and fibres.
- flanged joints can be used to join steel, cast iron, copper and plastic pipes. The flanges are made from steel, cast iron, bronze, copper, brass or plastic.
- welded joints can be used to join steel, copper and plastic pipes.

11.c.i Screwed joints

Screwed pipe joints can be made using fittings with parallel screw threads (Fig. **11.**11) or taper screw threads (Fig. **11.**12). These fittings are used for joining low carbon steel pipes.

11.c.ii Sleeved joints

- Sleeved joints for cast iron pipes (Figs. **11.**13 and **11.**14). Fig. **11.**14 shows three proprietary joints:
  Tyton joint – a self-anchored jointing system. The anchor gasket is made of natural rubber into which are moulded stainless steel teeth.
  Stantyte joint – a development of the Tyton joint that allows for some deflection (up to 3 to 4° in any direction and some axial movement). The gasket is made of ethylene-propylene rubber.
  Stanlock joint – a mechanical joint used for pipelines conveying gas. The seal is effected by compressing a wedge-shaped gasket of an elastomeric material, e.g. epichlorhydrin rubber, on to the jointing surfaces by means of a pressure gland and a series of nuts and bolts. This joint may be deflected up to 4° in any direction and it is capable of some axial movement.
- Sleeved joints for plastic pipes (Fig. **11.**15).

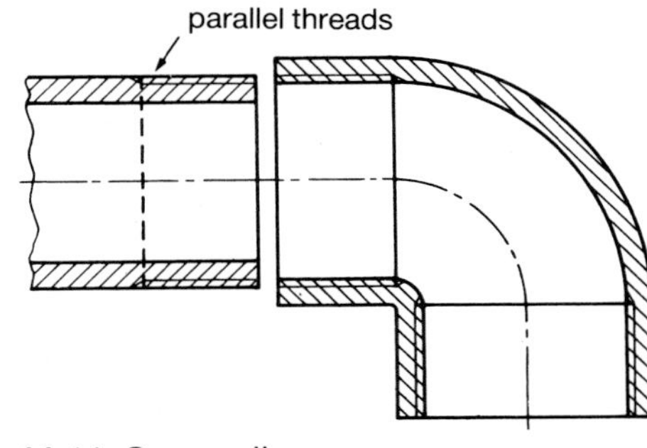

11.11 Screw elbow

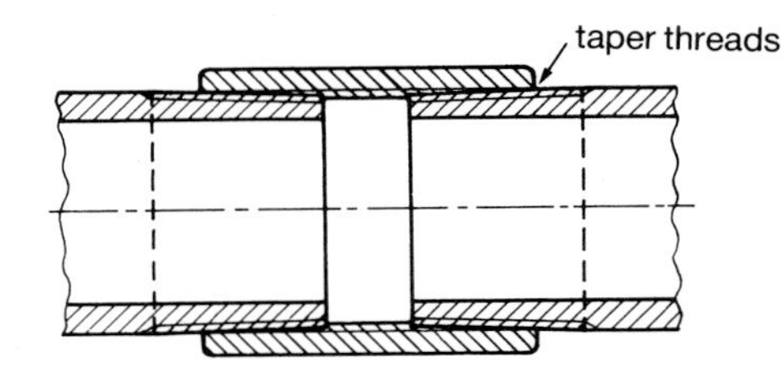

11.12 Fitting with taper threads

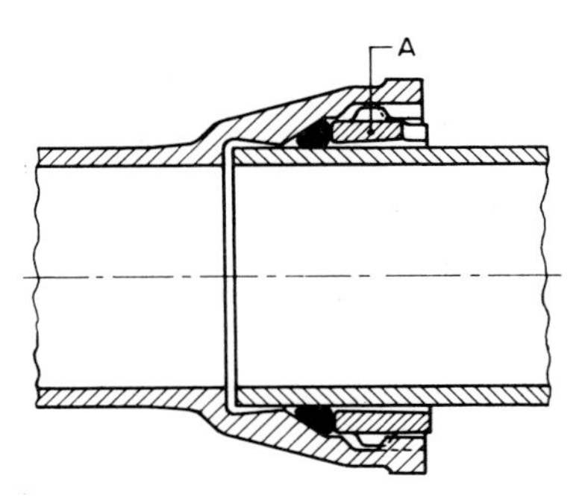

11.13 Sleeved joint with rubber seal

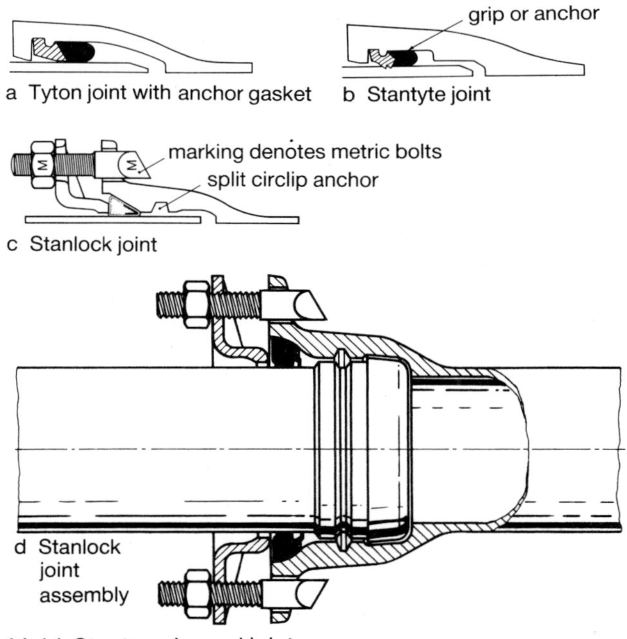

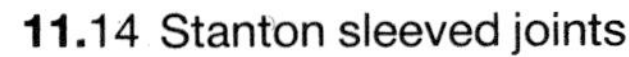

11.14 Stanton sleeved joints

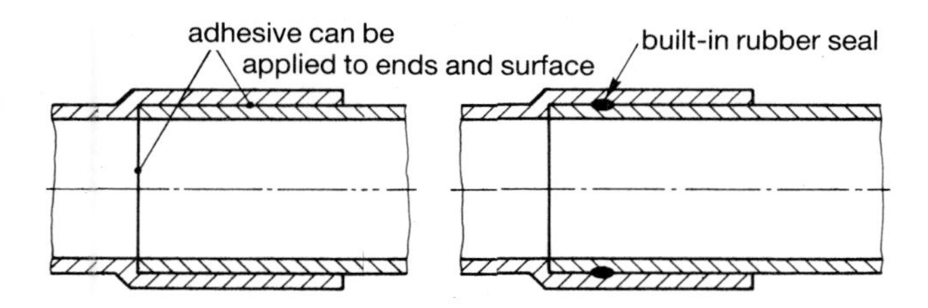

11.15 Sleeved joints for plastic pipes

11.c.iii Flanged joints

- Integral flanges (Fig. **11.**16) for cast iron pipes
- Welded flanges (Fig. **11.**17a, b and c) for steel and copper pipes
- Screwed flanges (Fig. **11.**18) for steel pipes

11.d The application of screwed joints

11.d.i Parallel screw threads

Fittings with parallel screw threads can be used for water and gas pipes (Fig. **11.**11).

11.d.ii Taper screw threads

Fittings with taper screw threads can be used for water, gas and steam pipes (Fig. **11.**12).

11.d.iii Special screw threaded fittings

Fittings with special screw threads are used for water, air, and oil, and are often termed compression fittings (Figs. **11.**19-**11.**21). They consist of internally tapered tube stops, tapered rings and tapered nuts.

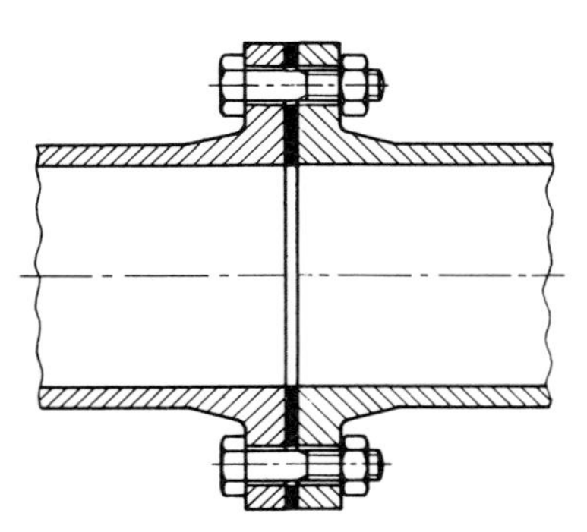

11.16 Flange joint with integral cast on flanges

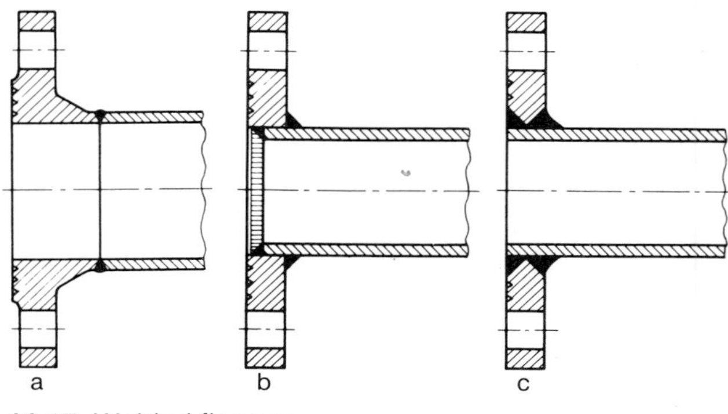

11.17 Welded flanges

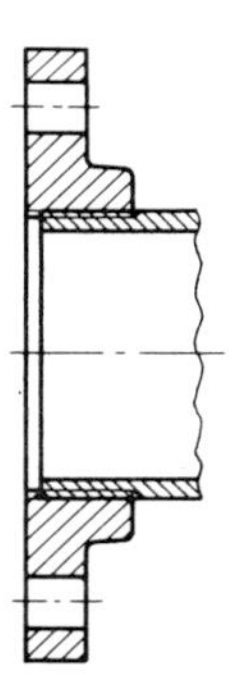

11.18 Screwed flange

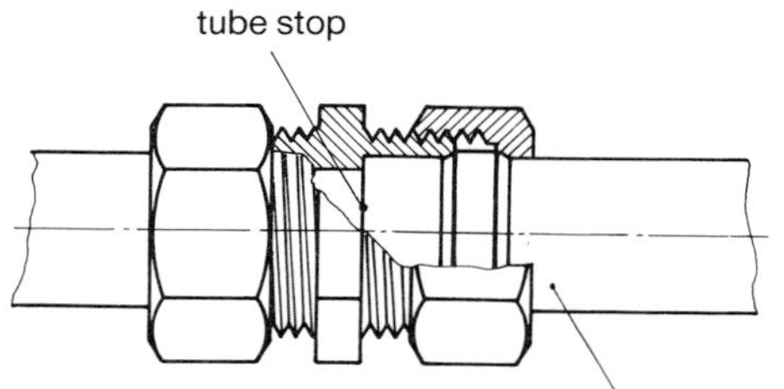

11.20 Compression fitting for waste pipe (sleeve bites into tube)

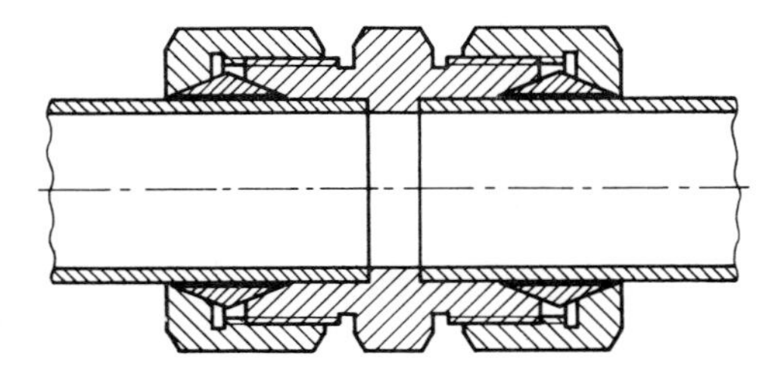

11.19 Compression fitting

alloy steel compression ring bites into seamless tube

11.21 Compression fitting for hydraulic tube

11.d.iv High pressure fittings

These may use either parallel or taper threaded joints; great care must be taken in sealing them. Fig. **11.**22 shows hydraulic joints with sealing arrangements.
Flexible tubes for high pressure are available in three pressure grades; low, medium and high. Special methods of compression are usually required to join the tube to the fitting. Fig. **11.**23 shows typical fittings, using pneumatic/hydraulic flexible tubing.

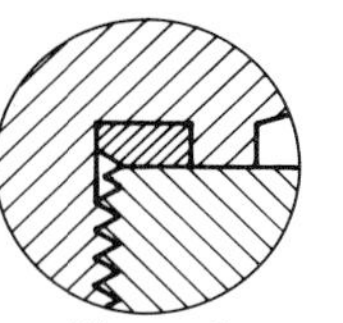

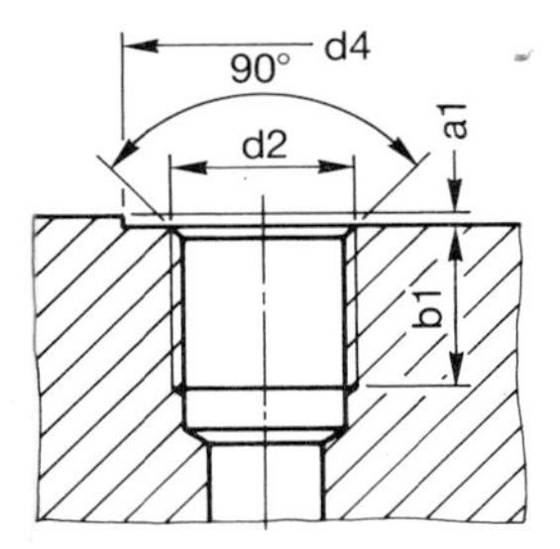

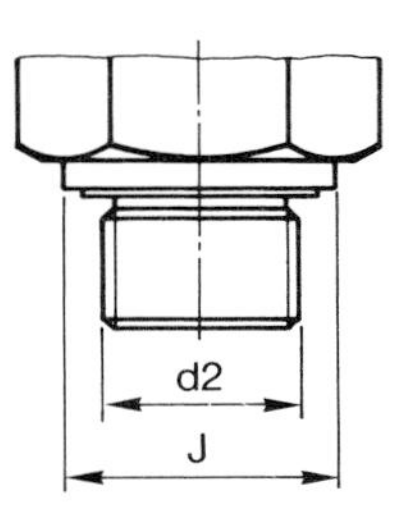

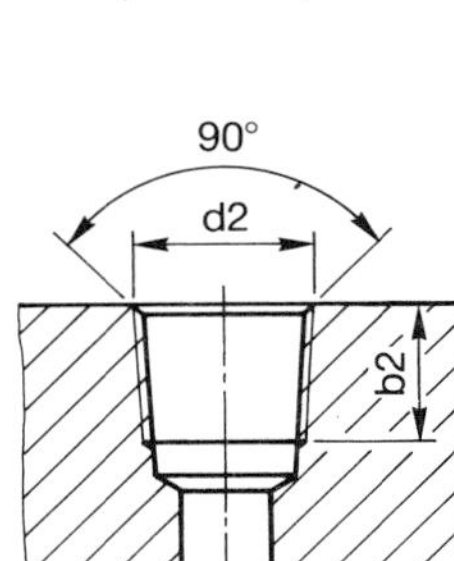

11.22 Hydraulic joint arrangements

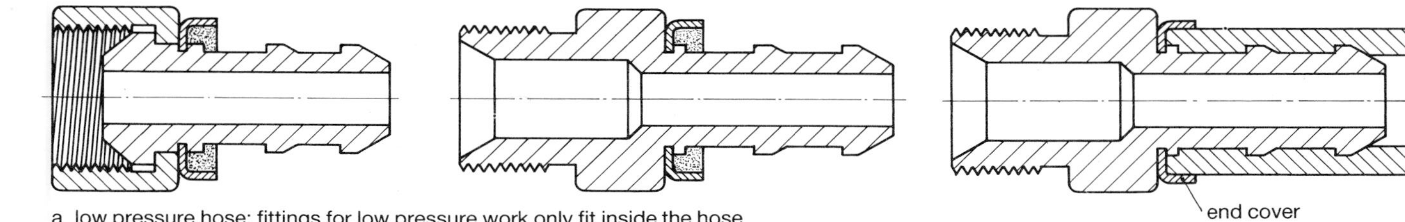

a low pressure hose: fittings for low pressure work only fit inside the hose

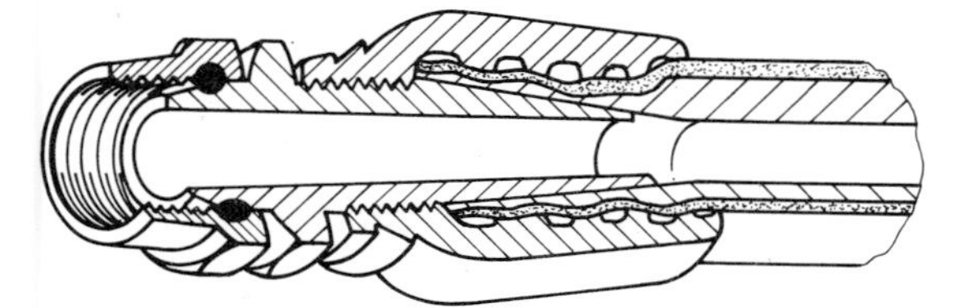

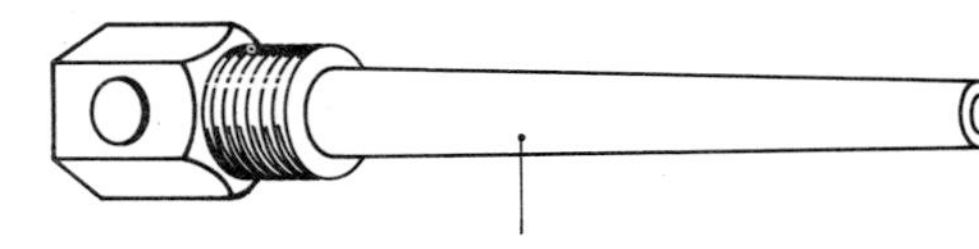

b medium pressure hose: fittings for medium pressure work fit both inside and outside the hose

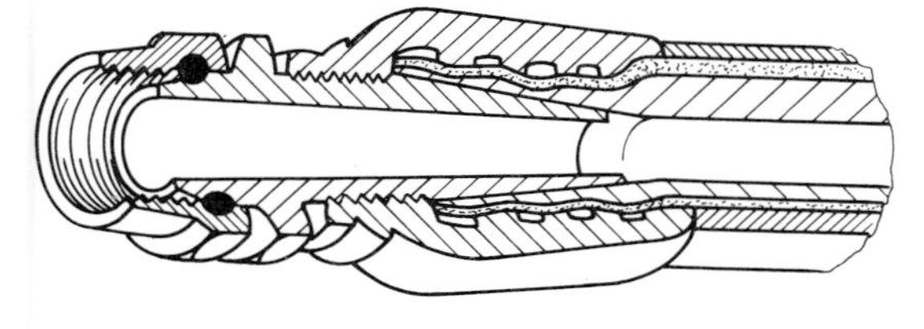

c high pressure hose: fittings for high pressure work fit inside the hose and around the metal reinforcement of the hose

11.23 Low, medium and high pressure hose fittings

11.e Sealing threaded joints

11.e.i Parallel screwed joints

These joints are sealed either with hemp and sealing compound or with sealing tape (Fig. **11**.24a). Hemp or tape should be wound in the direction of the thread i.e. left or right handed (Fig. **11**.24b).

11.e.ii Taper thread fittings

These fittings may be sealed with a sealing compound or tape.

11.e.iii Special screw threaded fittings or compression joints

With compression fittings the sealing faces between ring and tube should fit closely. The tapered ring, which can be made of plastic, brass or alloy steel, may be termed a sleeve, olive or ring. The ring is compressed by the tapers when the nut is tightened and may or may not 'bite' into the tube to provide the seal. Compression joints of this type can be used on plastic, copper and steel tubes which are usually associated with the relatively high pressures of fluid power, e.g. hydraulics. Figs. **11**.19-**11**.21 show various types and uses.

11.e.iv Hydraulic fittings

Those using threaded joints can be sealed as indicated in Fig. **11**.22 or with special screw threaded compression fittings.

11.f and g Sleeved joints – application and sealing

A rubber sealed sleeved joint is shown in Fig. **11**.13. The compression ring 'A' is turned at an angle of 45° so that the rubber is compressed to the sealing position. This and joints of the type shown in Fig. **11**.14 have superseded caulked joints using hemp and lead. Gasket or sealing materials include both natural and synthetic rubbers. These joints permit some misalignment and movement. Where necessary 'anchors' or grips will hold the pipes in position. Plastic pipes have a 'built-in' seal within the sleeve (Fig. **11**.15) or can be joined by adhesives. Plastic pipes are now replacing cast iron and other materials for many applications because they are cheap, easily installed, have adequate strength and are flexible.

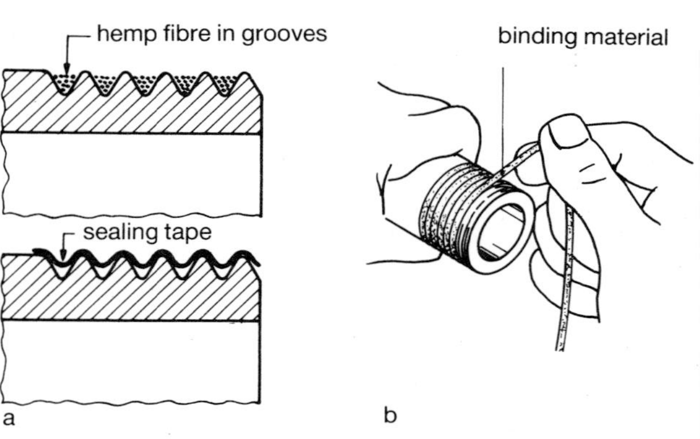

11.24 Sealing threads

11.h and i Flanged joints

Flanged joints are widely used and can withstand large forces without failure.

11.h.i Cast iron pipes and fittings: integral joints

These pipes always have integral cast iron flanges (Fig. **11**.16) whereas flanges for steel and copper pipes are separate and have to be fitted to pipes. (Fig. **11**.17).

11.h.ii-iv Steel and copper pipes: threaded and other joints

Flanges for these pipes can be fitted in one or other of the following ways:

- by a *screwed joint*. A screwed flange is shown in Fig. **11**.18; the threads may be parallel or tapered.
- by *soldering, brazing or welding*. A hard soldered joint is shown in Fig. **11**.25: bronze or steel flanges are either brazed or bronze welded on to copper pipes. Note that the joint requirements for these alternatives differ in that brazing requires a close fit so that capillary action can draw the material through to make a strong joint. The process also requires higher temperatures (Fig. **11**.26a and b).

  The welded joints shown in Fig. **11**.17a, b and c are being used more frequently because of the strength of the joint and because sealing is more positive.

- by *expanding*. As shown in Fig. **11.**27 joints of this type are still being used. The flanges are rolled on to the pipes by means of a pipe expander (Fig. **11.**28). The principle of operation is shown in Fig. **11.**29. Boiler tubes are a typical example of the use of this method.

11.i.i-iv Assembling flanged joints

When assembling pipes with this type of joint the following points should be noted:

- flange holes should not coincide with the vertical centre line. With corrosive contents even a small leakage could cause serious corrosion if the lowest bolt should lie on the centre line (Fig. **11.**30).
- flange faces should be parallel after tightening the bolts. If this is not achieved then distortion and leakage may occur.
- the appropriate type and thickness of packing must be inserted between the flange faces. Failure to ensure this may result in deterioration of the packing and leakage at the flange joint. Flanges with ground or scraped faces require no packing.
- bolts must be tightened in the proper sequence to avoid distorting the flanges (Fig. **11.**31).

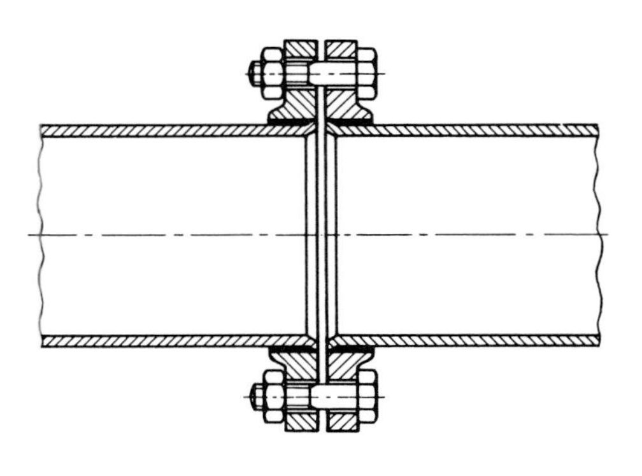

11.25 Soldered flange joint

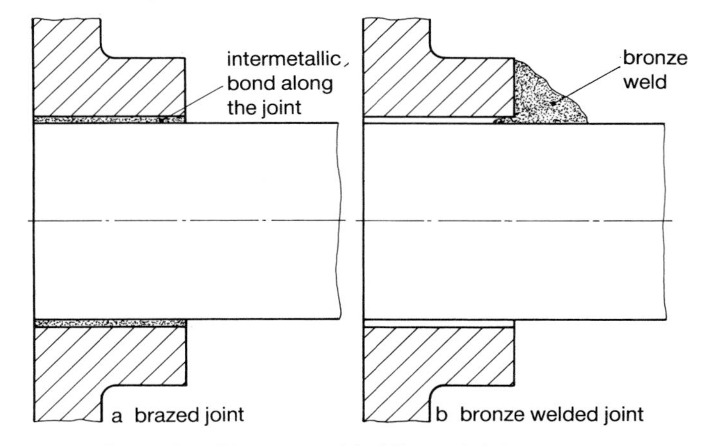

11.26 Brazed and bronze welded flange joints

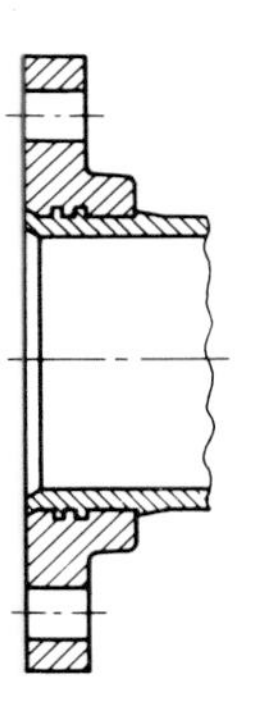

11.27 Rolled flange

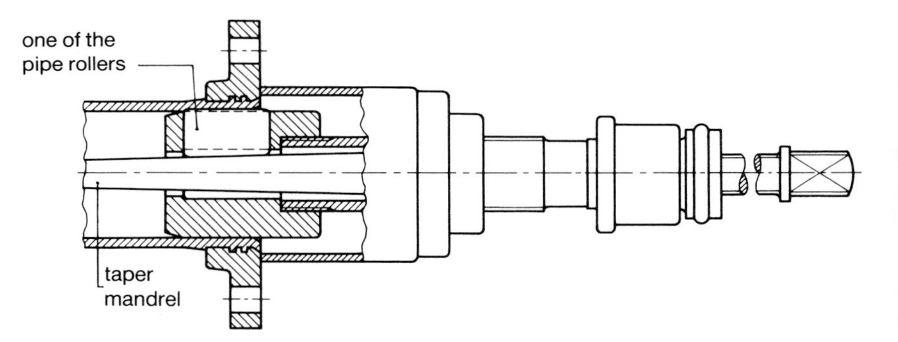

11.28 Pipe expander

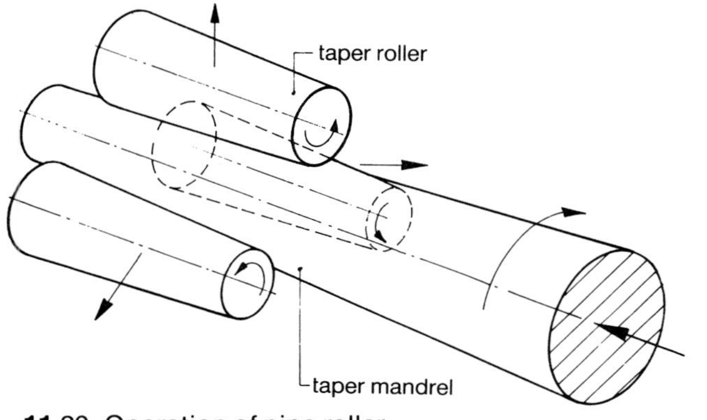

11.29 Operation of pipe roller

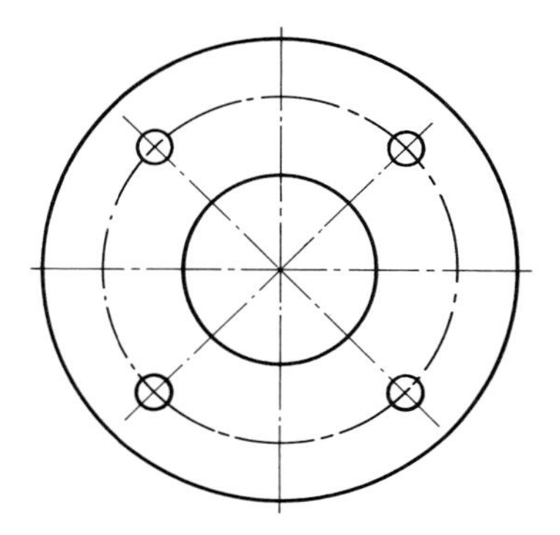

11.30 Flange holes not on the vertical centre line

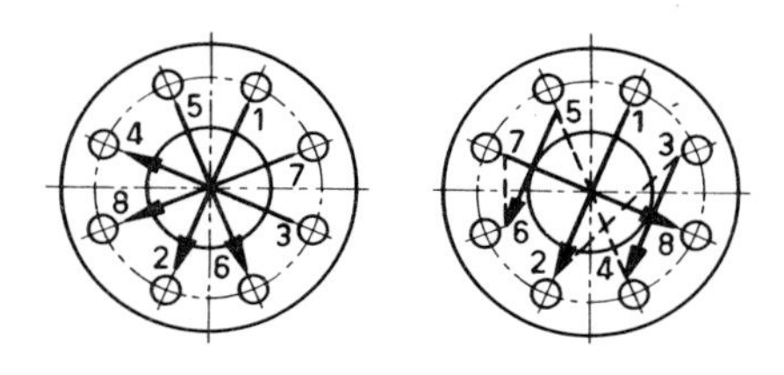

11.31 Sequence of tightening

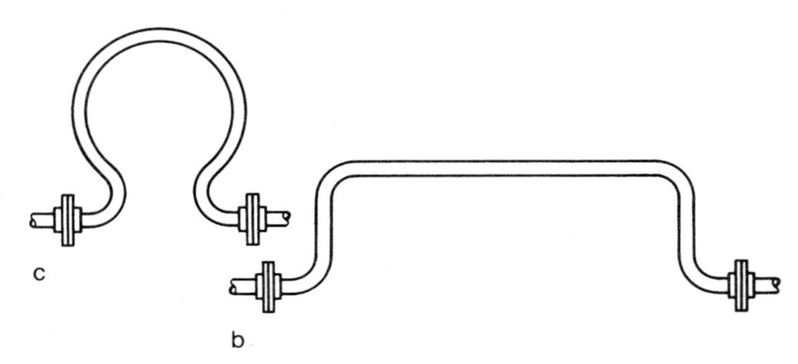

a

11.32 Expansion bends

11.j Temperature and expansion

Expansion must be taken into account in assembling pipes circulating hot water, steam or other hot substances. Neglect will result in substantial loads on the pipe and equipment flanges. A steel pipe expands in length 4 mm to the metre when the temperature rises 350 °C. In order to allow for expansion, expansion pipes are incorporated in the system (Fig. **11.**32a, b and c). Other devices are used to allow for expansion (Fig. **11.**33a, b and c). Horizontal pipe-lines are also supported on rolling devices to allow the pipes to move freely back and forth during expansion and contraction (Fig. **11.**34). Vertical movement is accommodated by devices such as that shown in Fig. **11.**35. Radial expansion should also be allowed for (Fig. **11.**36).

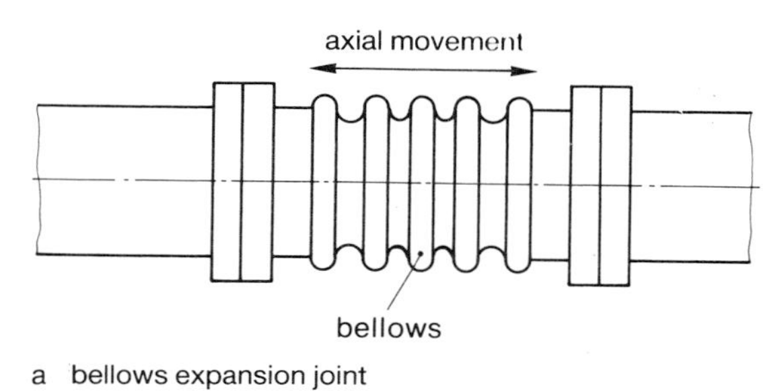

a bellows expansion joint

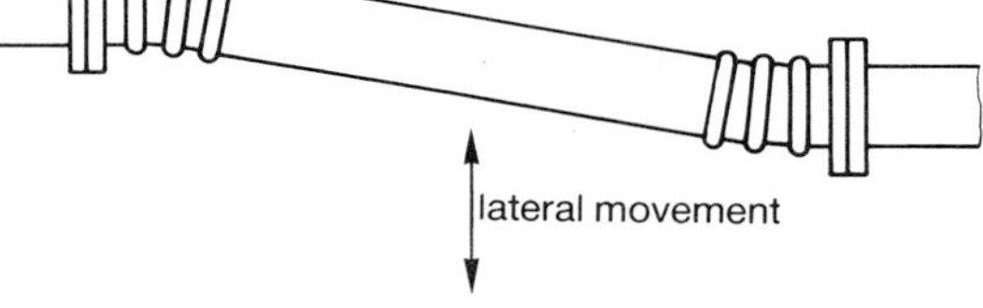

b joint for lateral movement

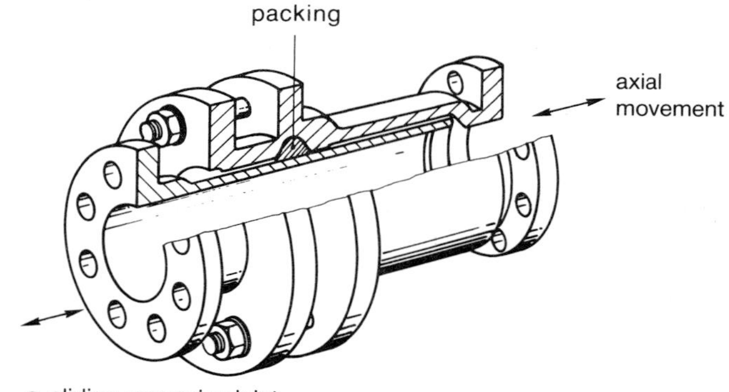

c sliding expansion joint

11.33 Other devices allowing for expansion

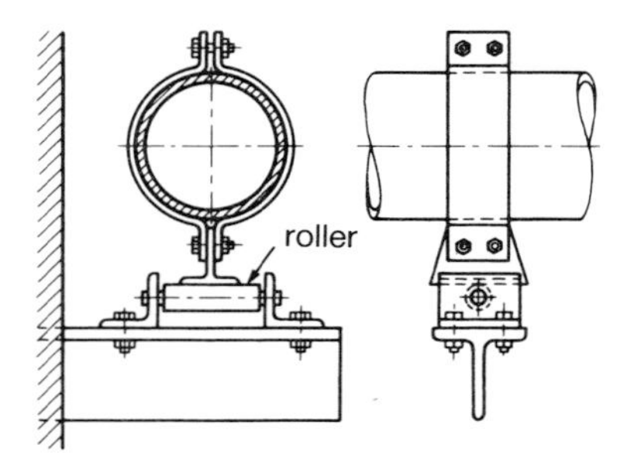

11.34 Support for horizontal pipe

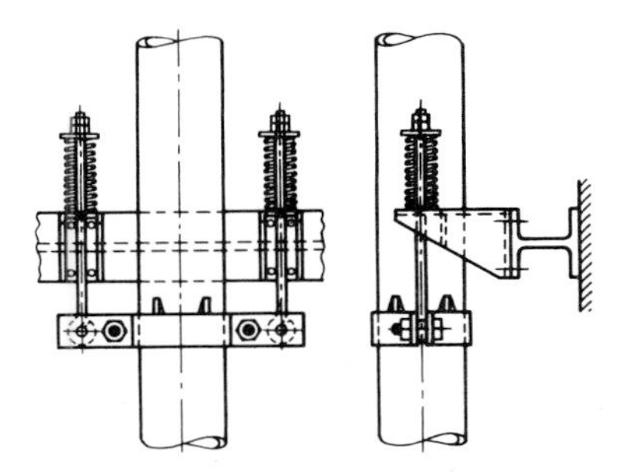

11.35 Attachment of horizontal pipe

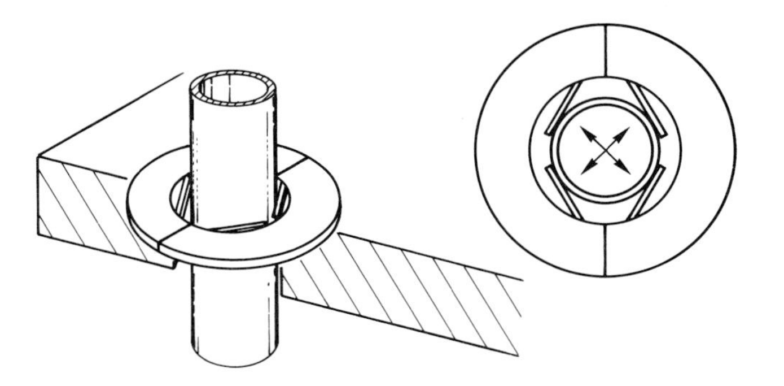

11.36 Ceiling plate permits radial expansion

11.k.i-v Connection of flanged pipes to system components

Before pipes are connected to system components such as valves or pumps, it is necessary to check that:

- the position of the flange face is correctly related to the centre line of the pipe (Fig. **11**.37)
- the pipe flange holes and the flange holes of the system component are aligned (Fig. **11**.38)
- the proper packing is available.

The pipes should then be adjusted so that the bearing faces of the flanges run parallel. After the gasket has been carefully placed between the flanges, and after the bolts have been checked to ensure that they are of the correct type and size, the nuts must be tightened in the proper sequence. Fig. **11**.39 shows pumps, valves and pipes which are all connected by flange joints. Fig. **11**.40 illustrates that flange joints are also used for large tubes.

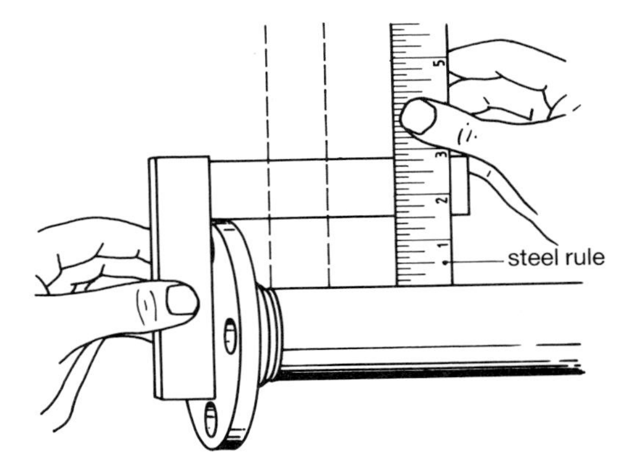

11.37 Alignment of flange faces

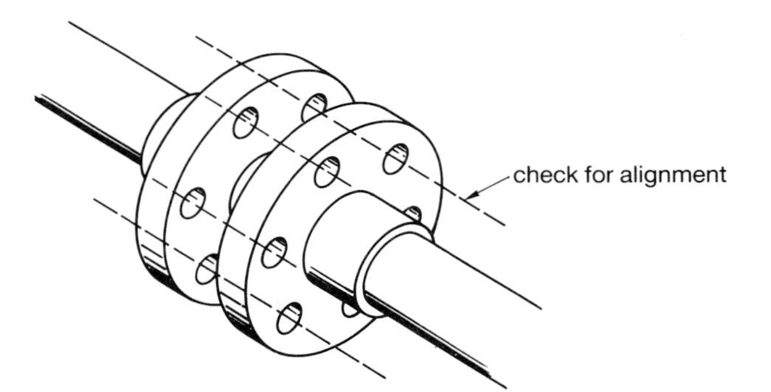

11.38 Alignment of holes

11.40 Large flange joints

11.39 Flange joints

12 The dismantling of pipework systems

Many points raised in the discussion about pipe assembling (Section 11) are equally relevant in the context of their dismantling. First, we shall consider why dismantling a section of pipework may be necessary.

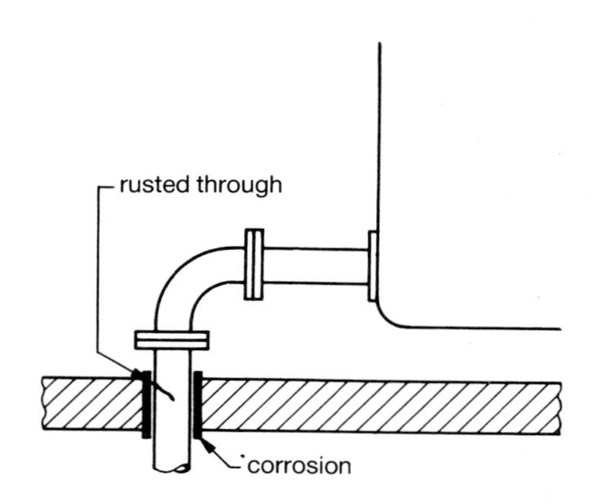

12.1 Local corrosion

12.a.i-iv The purpose of dismantling

This may be because

- a pipe is corroded or has suffered local damage (Fig. **12**.1)
- a modification has to be made in an existing pipe layout (Fig. **12**.2a and b)
- the repair or overhaul of a system component, such as a valve or a compressor, is necessary and this can involve dismantling part of the pipework system
- a pipe is blocked.

12.b Factors affecting preparation for dismantling

Given good maintenance, most dismantling operations can be timed to suit plant operating needs. Even in an emergency, some regard must be paid to the operational situation and other important factors controlling how the work is to be done. All or many of the following points may be relevant.

12.b.i Shut down time

In factory systems the time available for shut down is usually very limited and therefore dismantling and reassembling must be kept to a minimum. This will have a bearing on most if not all of the constraints and requirements mentioned under in this section. 12.b.ii to 12.b.v.

12.b.ii Operational sequence

A correct sequence must be pre-planned and must include any 'Permit to Work' procedures necessary (as mentioned in Section 8.e).

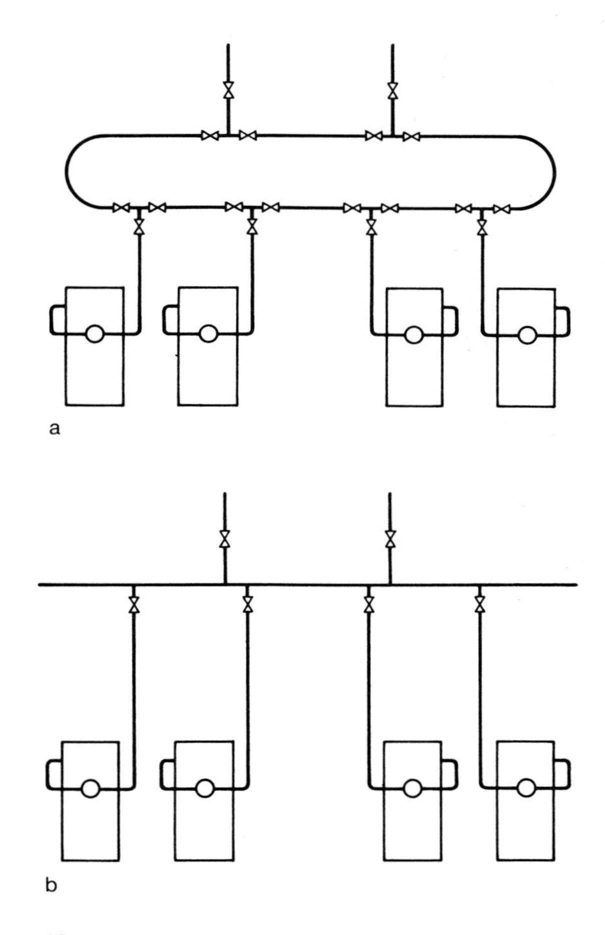

12.2 Alteration to existing pipework systems

12.b.iii Prefabrication of new sections

New sections which are to be installed must be prefabricated and be available on the spot for installation or connection.

12.b.iv Availability of tools, equipment and materials

Everything required including auxiliary tools and joining materials (like new bolts, gaskets, etc.) must be present on site.

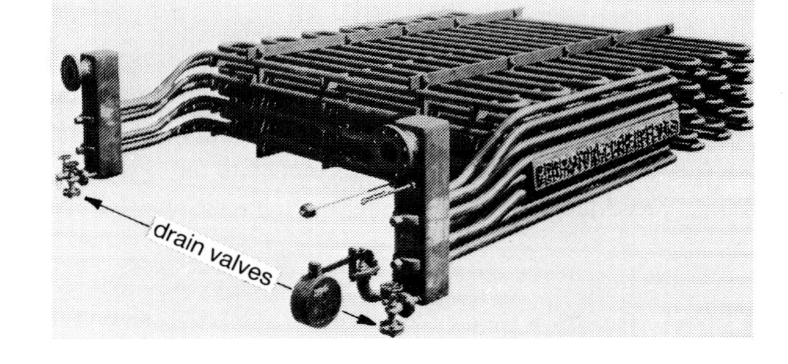

12.3 System draining

12.b.v Shut down procedures

Shut down, exhausting, draining and purging procedures must be planned, i.e.:

- supply pipes must be shut off and made pressure-free. Careful planning at this stage must include the identification of contents within the pipe. Reference to British Standard 1710 should be made and any necessary action taken into account.
- pipes for the circulation of liquids must be shut off and drained at the lowest point. See Fig. **12**.3 and the additional details given in the Appendix.
- pipes (also tanks or vessels) which have been exhausted or drained of liquids or gases which are dangerous to health, must in addition be purged of all traces of the liquid or gas. Some information on the procedure for purging pipes is included in the Appendix (Ap.2.b).
- machines must be rendered safe to work on, e.g. some need to be put into a 'no-pressure' and safe situation. Figs. **12**.4 and **12**.5 show a press which uses high pressure oil for power transmission. Even after electrical isolation (locking-off, etc.) a press can be extremely dangerous unless it is placed in the correct safe position as indicated in Fig. **12**.4. Detailed information on such procedures may be obtained from relevant Health and Safety Executive regulations published by HMSO.

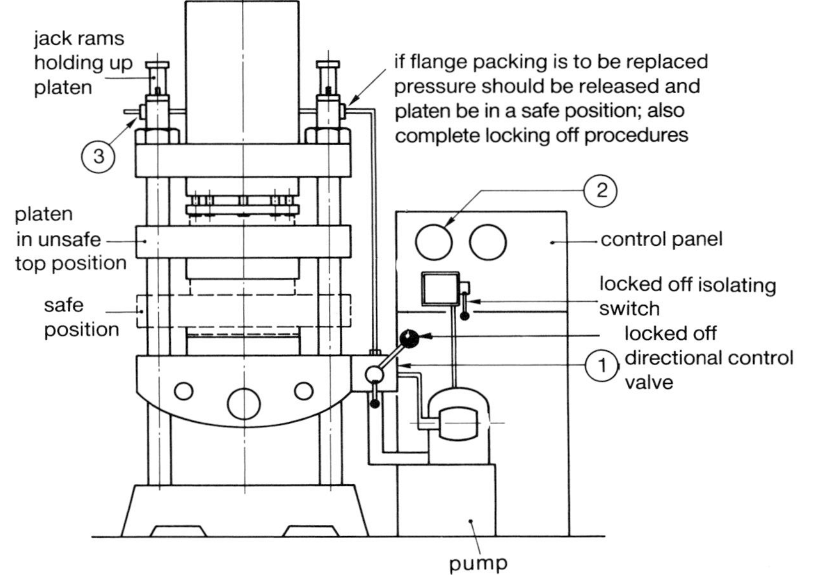

12.4 Hydraulic press

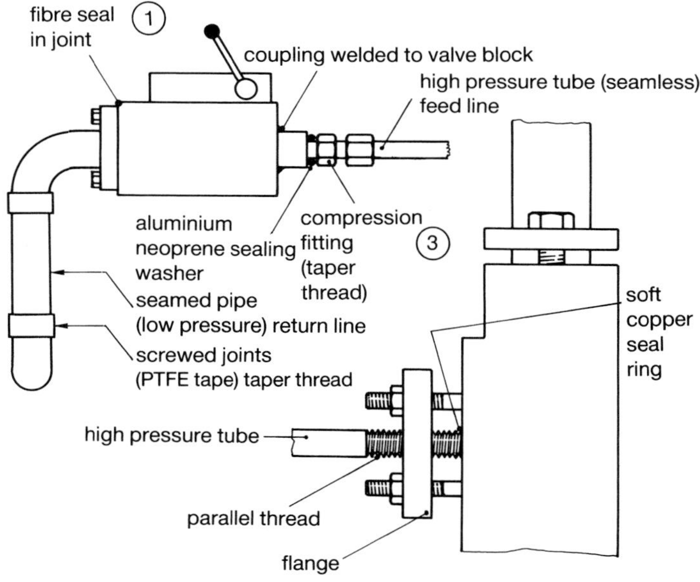

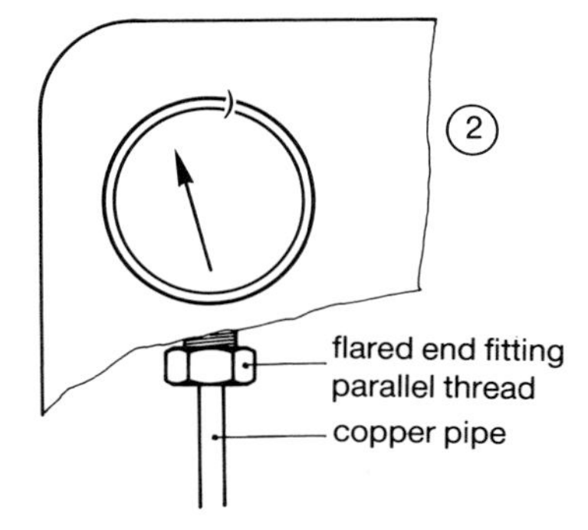

12.5 Details of hydraulic press (fig. 12.4)

12.b.vi Safety precautions

All measures must be observed, including measures to prevent inadvertent or premature operation of the dismantled section, i.e. placing of blank flanges, 'locked off' valves, 'locked off' switches, etc. Strict adherence to the 'Permit to Work' procedures is of the utmost importance.

12.b.vii Isolation procedures

It is important to note that when maintenance operations are being carried out on a section of pipework within an extensive system it is not necessary to close down the whole system. System design will perhaps accommodate section shut-off without affecting the whole system. Before attempting any dismantling, therefore, it is necessary that the system design specification should be consulted and any instructions relevant to section isolation should be carried out.

12.c Screwed pipe joints

Pipework systems with screwed pipe joints will have been assembled in a certain sequence and should be dismantled in the reverse order of that sequence. It is not always possible or practicable to unscrew the part that has to be replaced, e.g. it may be a middle section. In these circumstances the pipe may have to be sawn or flame cut in at least one place, if this is practicable. The part to be removed can then be unscrewed. For subsequent joining of the new section, joints shown in Fig. **12.6** may be used. This fitting is a hexagon union. With care most screwed components can be re-used as long as there is no thread or corrosion damage. Female socketed components are prone to 'swelling' of the threaded portion nearest the lip of the component. This is due to the male taper screw 'squeezing' out the female thread on tightening. To avoid leakage, components with these faults should not be re-used.

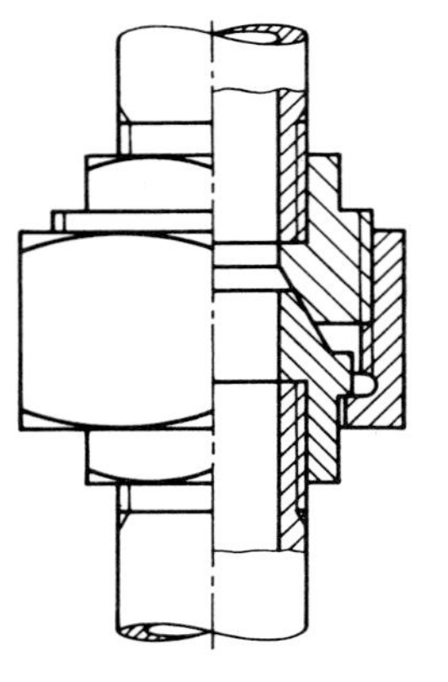

12.6 Hexagon union

12.d Flanged pipe joints

Pipes with flat face flanges can be removed easily from the pipework system (Fig. **12.7**). Dismantling becomes more difficult when the pipes have been connected by male and female flange joints. The pipe has to be moved a distance of at least twice the depth of the recess before it can be removed (Fig. **12.8**).
Old packing has to be completely removed from the flange faces before new gaskets are installed.
Old bolts, when removed, should be inspected for defects before re-use (Fig. **12.9**). Using defective bolts could lead to the joint failing, with dangerous or other harmful results (Fig. **12**.10). Dimensions and quality of new bolts must be checked for suitability and, where relevant, must be to the required specification.

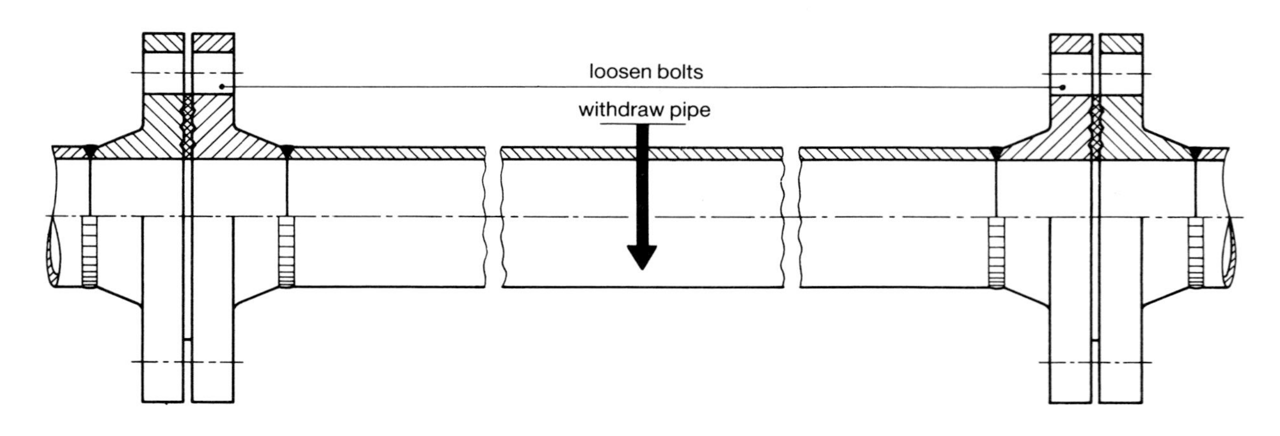

12.7 Flat faced flanges

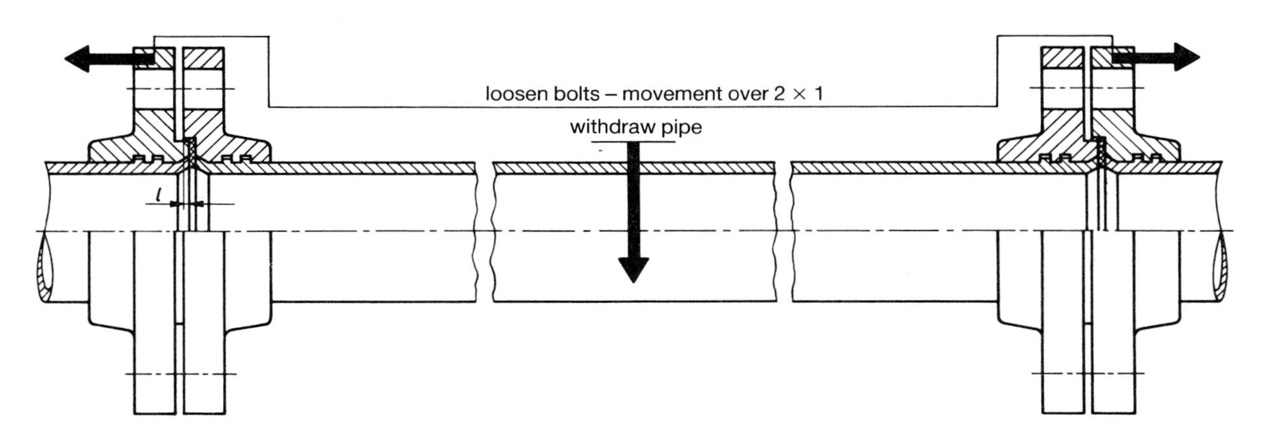

12.8 Flange joints with spigots and recesses

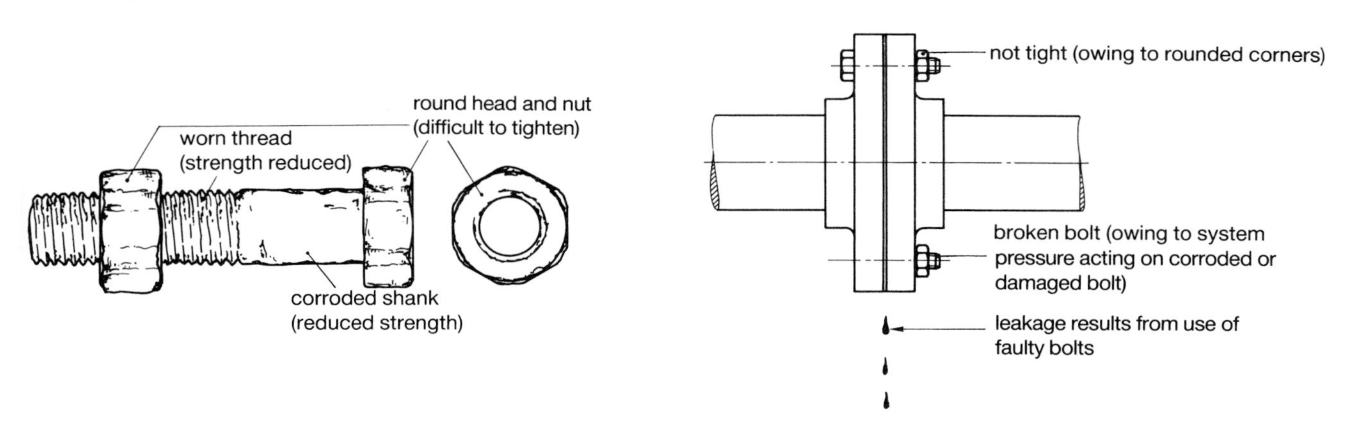

12.9 Faults on bolts (visual inspection)

12.10 Some effects of faulty bolts and nuts

Appendix

Details in this appendix cover the following items:

- engineering drawings, a brief explanation; for further information and to enable you to read and interpret them refer to the series book *Interpreting Drawings, Specifications and Data*.
- Emptying and purging pipework systems; some notes in extension of the text in Section 12.b.v.

Ap.1 Engineering drawings

Engineering drawings give information about shapes, dimensions, surface finishes, materials, assemblies and connections of components.
They enable the reader to understand what has to be done, either to make, lay out or assemble an infinite variety of engineering plant and products. The drawings are therefore invaluable in the processes of assembling and dismantling.

As can be seen from Fig. **Ap.**1 the main forms of drawings include:

- general arrangement: these show the complete arrangements of all the components (Figs. **Ap.**2 and **Ap.**3)
- sub-assembly: here greater detail shows the way parts are assembled (Fig. **Ap.**4)
- detail drawings: these give the detail needed to make the item (Fig. **Ap.**5).

Engineering drawings may be produced by hand or computer (Computer Assisted Drawing – C.A.D.). Note that both Fig. **Ap.**3 and Fig. **Ap.**5 are of C.A.D. type. Numbering or coding usually starts with that of the general arrangement, other numbers being added to it progressively thereafter. Copying is commonly by the dye line process or photocopying.

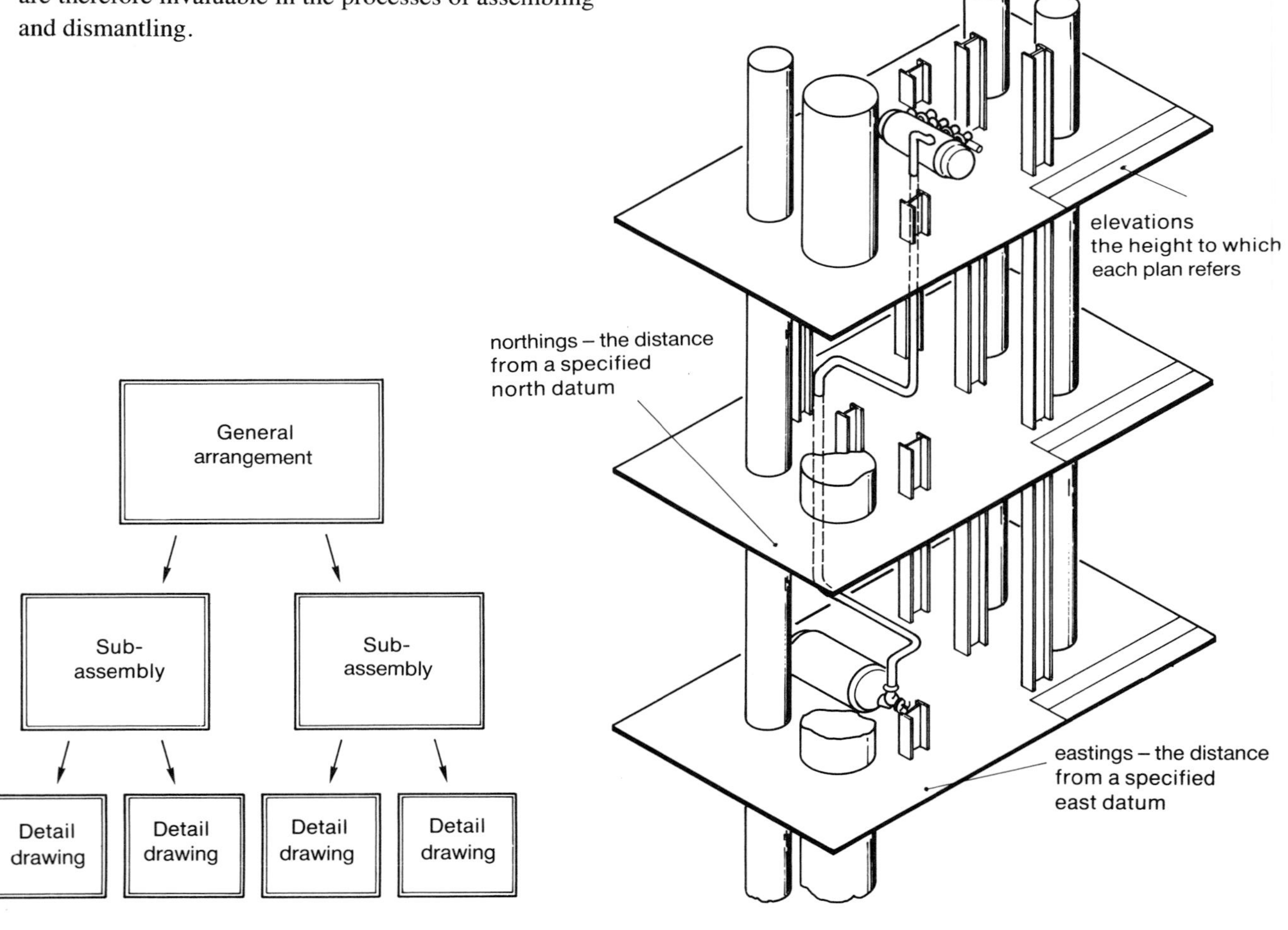

Ap.1 The main forms of engineering drawings

Ap.2 General arrangement drawing (piping plan)

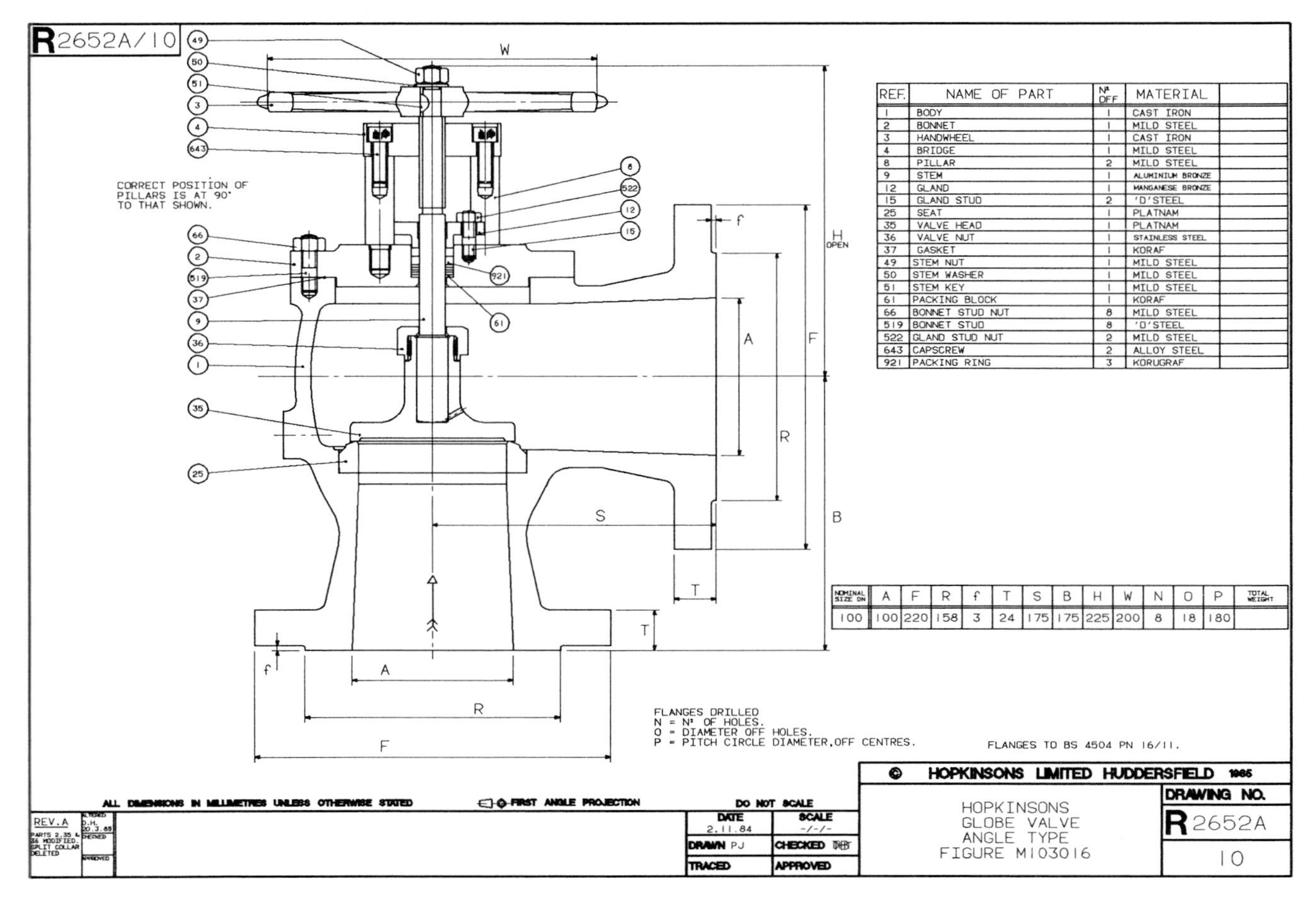

Ap.3 General arrangement drawing

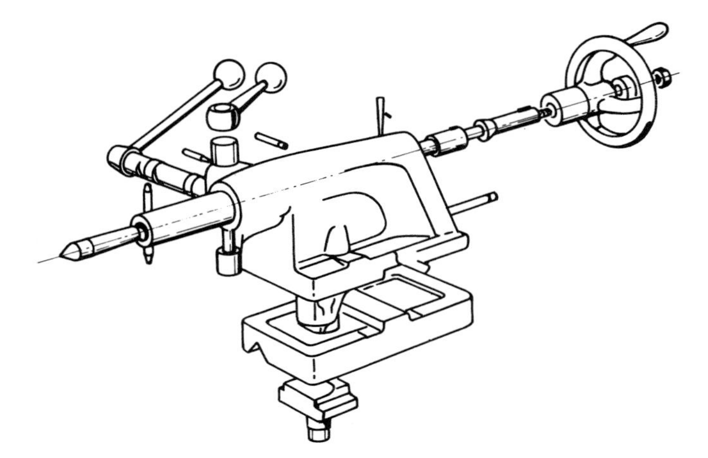

Ap.4 Loose-head of a lathe

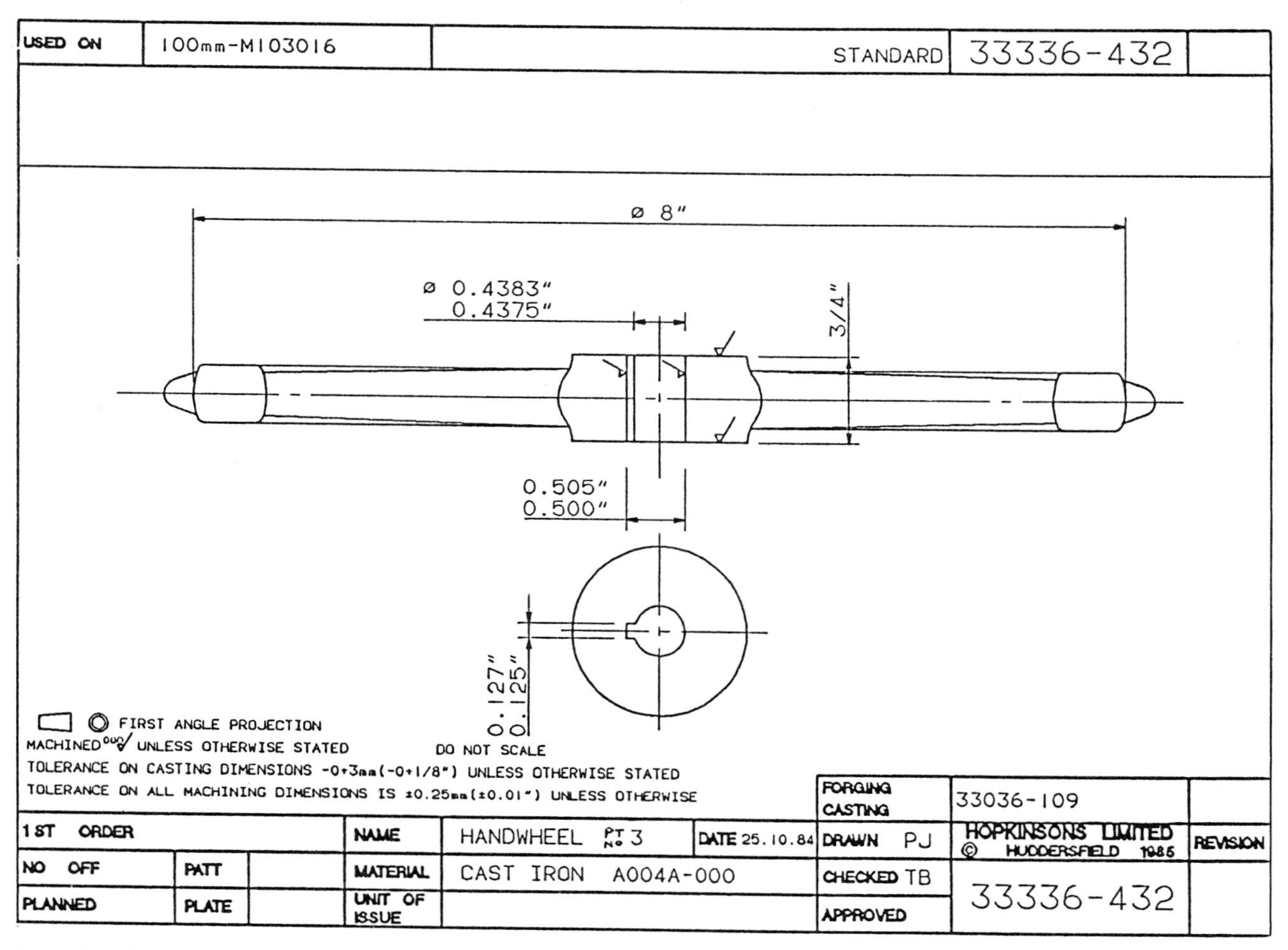

Ap.5 Detail drawing

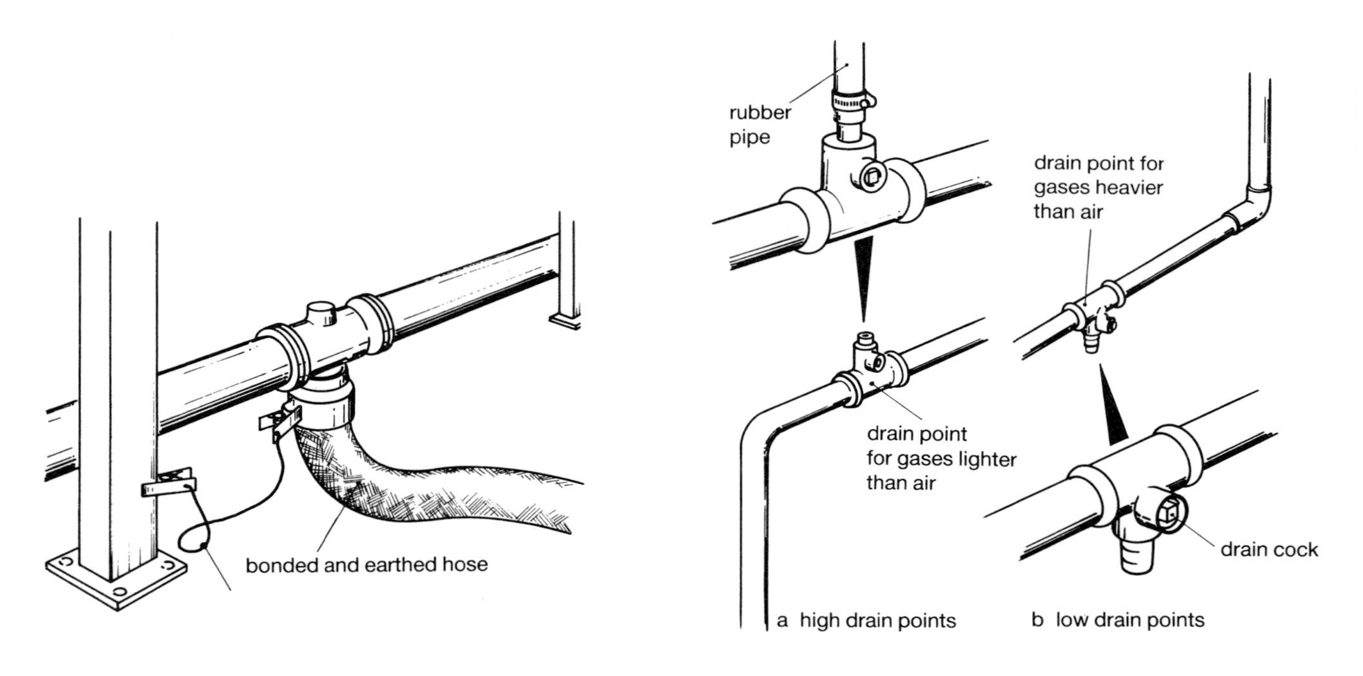

Ap.6 Hose, bonded and earthed

Ap.7 Drain points

Ap.2 Emptying and purging pipework systems

Ap.2.a Emptying pipework

The details following should be read as an extension of the text under 12.b.v. dealing with shutting off and draining the system and 12.b.vi dealing with safety.

The method of emptying depends on the contents and the environment of the pipework. Methods used for dangerous liquids and gases must conform to the Factories Acts and any local regulations concerning them.

Table **Ap.1** gives a general summary of operations dealing separately with liquids and gases. Examples of procedural points for some particular fluids are:

- *Water*: This is normally safe, but if it is at high temperature or pressure, or it is in an environment where it could cause damage, special precautions must be taken. Normally, it can be drained into a suitable tank or sewer.
- *Petrol*: This must be drained into a special container and the pipework purged to remove the remaining traces of the liquid and vapour.
  Ensure that there are no naked flames in the vicinity.
- *Nitrogen*: This can be allowed to escape into the

Table Ap.1 Draining liquids and removing gases

Operations	Draining liquids	Removing gases
Observing safety and special rules	Comply with any special rules which apply to the liquid carried in the system; e.g. a bonded and correctly earthed hose must be used when pumping liquids which ignite easily, to avoid collecting static electricity which may discharge and cause a fire (Fig. **Ap**.6).	Comply with any special rules which apply to the gas in the system, e.g. **when dealing with an irritant gas or toxic gas a respirator must be worn.**
Making connections	Connect a suitable hose at one end to a pumping unit and, at the other, to the drain point of the pipework. Connect the outlet of the pumping unit to a suitable tank or drain. Small sections of pipework can often be drained without using a pumping unit.	• A gas lighter than air: the drain point will be at the highest point of the pipework (Fig. **Ap**.7.a) • A gas heavier than air: the drain point will be at the lowest point (Fig. **Ap**.7.b) • A safe gas at high pressure (e.g. compressed air): make a temporary pipe connection to a place where the pressure can be released safely. Ensure that the temporary pipe is securely held down so that it cannot 'flail' (Fig. **Ap**.8). • A gas at low pressure: attach the hose of a suitable pumping unit to the drain point of the system.
Venting	Open the air inlet valves of the pipework to allow air to replace the liquid removed.	Open the air inlet valve most remote from the pump.
Pumping or draining	Pump or drain the liquid out of the pipework.	Pump the gas into a container.

atmosphere, provided ventilation is good and the gas can disperse.

- *Ammonia*: Wear compressed air breathing apparatus. Wear rubber boots, rubber gauntlets and goggles; if large quantities have to be handled, wear a PVC suit as well. Keep upwind of the system.
  Ensure that there are no naked flames.
  Drain the ammonia into a special sump together with constant running water to flush away the ammonia. Ensure that the end of the pipe in the sump is not submerged in water. Purging is necessary; generally it should follow the procedure outlined in Ap.2.b, if possible using dry nitrogen or otherwise dry air. The purged waste must be discharged to the atmosphere for dispersal without causing harm.

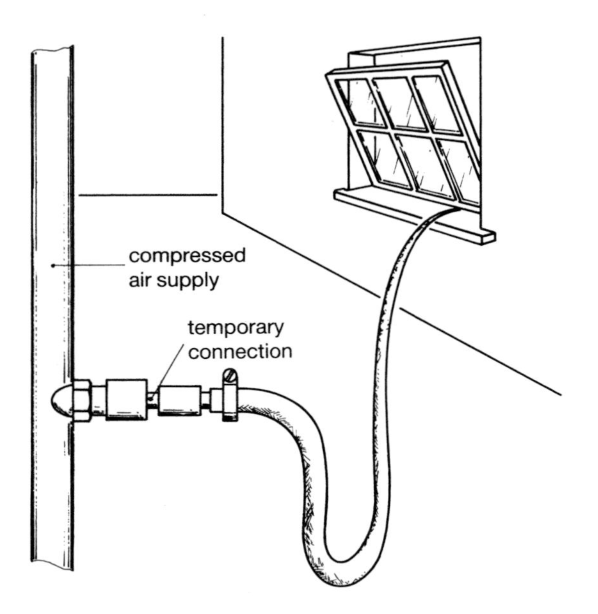

Ap.8 Temporary pipe connection

Ap.2.b Purging pipework

Any liquid or gas which is a hazard to health must be evacuated before pipework is dismantled. A variety of purging agents is used, e.g. steam, nitrogen or carbon dioxide, depending on the pipework contents.

The procedure for purging with steam is as follows:

- place portable containers under the drain valves, fit suitable pipes to them, leading them to a site where steam can be safely discharged
- connect an inlet union on the pipework to a low pressure steam supply (Fig. **Ap**.9)
- turn on the steam supply
- purge the system until all hazardous material has been removed
- shut off and disconnect the steam supply
- remove the drainage vessels and dispose of the waste. Note that it is essential to comply with any special regulations concerning its disposal, **e.g. flammable liquids must not be discharged into ordinary drainage sewers**.

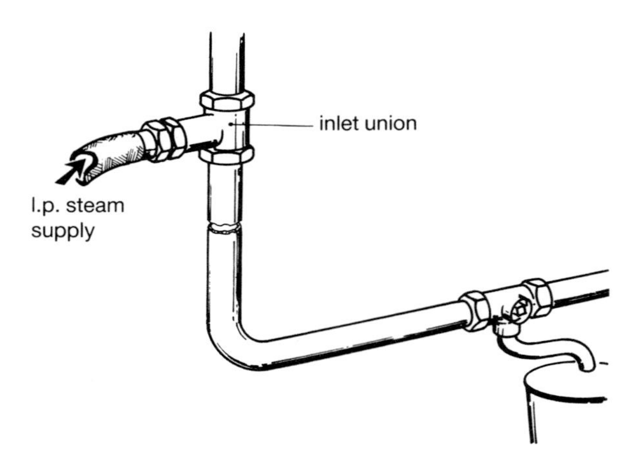

Ap.9 Connection to an inlet union

Acknowledgements

The publishers gladly record their thanks to the following contributors who have kindly supplied material for inclusion in this book:

Austin Rover, Figs. **2**.5, **2**.6 and **3**.4; Buck & Hickman who gave permission to reproduce the following line illustrations: Figs. **5**.27a, **6**.22, **6**.24, **7**.9a and **7**.21 from their 1986-88 catalogue; Haynes Workshop Manual, Figs. **10**.7a and **10**.7b; Colchester Lathe Co., **10**.8; Hydraulic & Fluid Control Co. Ltd., Fig. **11**.2; Stanton & Staveley, Fig. **11**.14; Legris, Fig. **1**.22; Harrison Lathes, Fig. **Ap**.4; Hopkinsons Ltd., Figs. **3**.3 and **3**.5.

Technology of Skilled Processes

Basic Engineering
Competences 201

Assembling and Dismantling

Practice and test questions

Published as a
co-operative venture
between
Stam Press Ltd

and

City and Guilds

Practice and test questions

The questions in this book are intended to help the student achieve and demonstrate a knowledge and understanding of the subject matter which it covers. Accordingly, the questions follow the original section order, under the same headings. Finally there are questions spanning the sections and approximating to the level of those in the relevant examination of the City and Guilds of London Institute.

First published in Great Britain 1987
as a co-operative venture between Stam Press Ltd. and the City and Guilds of London Institute

Reprinted 1988

Printed and bound in Great Britain by Martin's of Berwick

ASSEMBLING AND DISMANTLING Name: ______________________ Class: ________ Number: _____

1 Introduction to assembling and dismantling

The following questions relate to the first section of the book, but what is said here about answering them *also* applies to similar questions covering later sections.
Many questions (e.g. 1) provide a number of possible answers, usually four, lettered a, b, c and d. Unless otherwise indicated, only *one* is correct and you are required to decide which it is and show by circling the appropriate letter(s) or number(s).

Example
When planning the assembly of a small component it is important to establish:
a the material from which the parts are made
ⓑ the correct sequence for fitting the parts
c power supply voltage
d transport requirements

Answers to questions where you are asked to state specific information (e.g. 12 and 13) should be short and clear.

---

1 Connecting separate parts to form a whole structure, system or component is termed:

a dismantling
b assembling
c ascertaining
d structuring

Refer to Fig. 1.1 in order to answer this question.

2 State THREE possible consequences of the screw being inserted before the pulley is correctly positioned on the shaft.

____

____

____

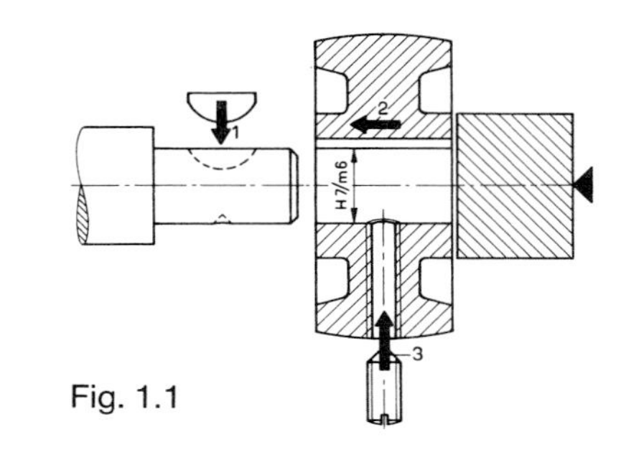

Fig. 1.1

Refer to Fig. 1.2 in order to answer questions 3 and 4.

3 A clean, adequately filled and heated oil bath, and the appropriate safety equipment are essential factors to be considered when:
a using a hydraulic oil press to fit the bearings
b planning a method of fitting the bearings
c lubricating the shaft so that the bearing slips on easily
d dismantling the shaft and bearings

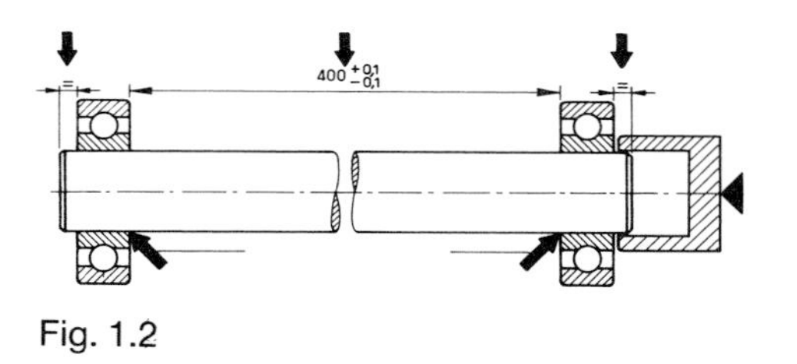

Fig. 1.2

---

4 The positioning of the bearings is to be:
a 11 mm
b $400 \begin{smallmatrix}+.03\\-.01\end{smallmatrix}$ from the centre of the shaft
c $400 \begin{smallmatrix}+.03\\-.01\end{smallmatrix}$ from the centre of the shaft plus bearings width
d the same distance from their respective shaft ends

Refer to Fig. 1.3 in order to answer questions 5 and 6

5 The diagram indicates
a an integral flange coupling with holes drilled at 45° to axis
b a disc coupling with holes drilled at 45° to axis
c a welded flange coupling with holes drilled at 45° to axis
d a sleeved coupling with holes drilled at 45° to axis

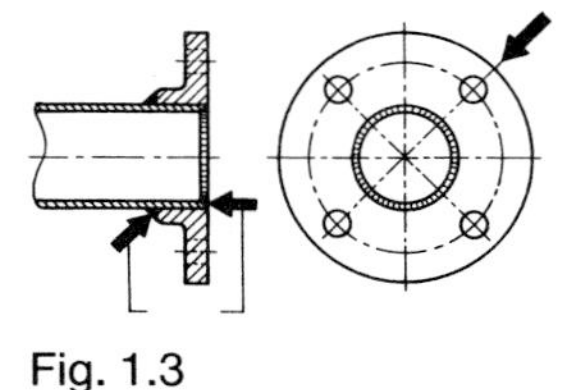
Fig. 1.3

---

6 The position of the holes is important because:
a they must be placed only at a standardised 45° to the axis
b correct alignment with other mating components which have been drilled in advance is assured
c at the angle shown they are more convenient for bolt tightening
d distortion of bolts and flange faces is better controlled

Refer to Fig. 1.1 in order to answer question 7

7 To achieve the required interference fit, the shaft diameter is greater than the hole diameter in the pulley. If the exact sizes had not been decided beforehand:
a the pulley hole could have been too large for the shaft to fit correctly
b the pulley hole could have been too small for the shaft to fit correctly
c the conditions of fit described in a, b, or d would have meant the parts would have had to be modified to provide the correct fit
d the shaft could have been too large for the hole to fit correctly

---

8 During assembly, plastic caps are often found covering holes. Which of the following describes their function correctly?
a they are part of the assembly
b they are to identify the component type
c they are to protect the component from harmful particles entering the system
d they are to identify the hole number

---

9 Indicate the exception to the general rule that in design dismantling must be a consideration.
a 'throw away' assemblies
b guaranteed parts
c stainless steel assemblies
d extra-life components

---

10 State THREE reasons why an assembly may be dismantled.

____

____

____

Refer to Fig. 1.5 in order to answer this question.

11 The parts likely to wear most are:
a the keys holding the gears
b the bolts securing the chain sprocket
c the gear and chain driving teeth
d the chain joining clips

Fig. 1.5

---

12 Give short and clear answers to the following questions:
a State the purpose of assembly.
b List SIX important factors that should be taken into consideration prior to assembling, giving reasons why you consider these to be important.

2 Methods

The following questions relate to the above subject. Answers should be given as explained on Page 75.

1 In a hydraulic system the valve is bolted to the control panel and is then connected by tubes to the press, which has already been assembled on site. If the pipes have to be bent and then cut to length before fitting, the method of assembly is called
a 'one off' assembly
b on site batch production
c hydraulic system assembly line production with fabrication
d partial fabrication, fitting and assembling on site

Refer to Fig. 2.1 in order to answer questions 2 and 3.

2 After stage 4 of the pump assembly, the pump:
a requires to be moved in a direction indicated by the arrow
b is in a state where all checks and adjustments have been made and it is ready for industrial use
c is at the start of the assembly process
d should be checked for correct operation

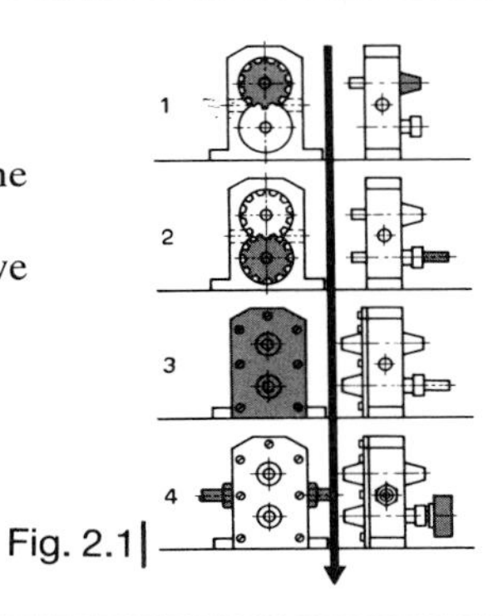

Fig. 2.1

3 The method of assembly indicated in Fig. 2.1 is:
a 'batch assembly'
b 'one off' assembly
c partial fabrication assembly
d assembly line assembly

Refer to Fig. 2.2 in order to answer this question.

4 The number of identical parts used on the assemblies is:
a 12
b 24
c 6
d 3

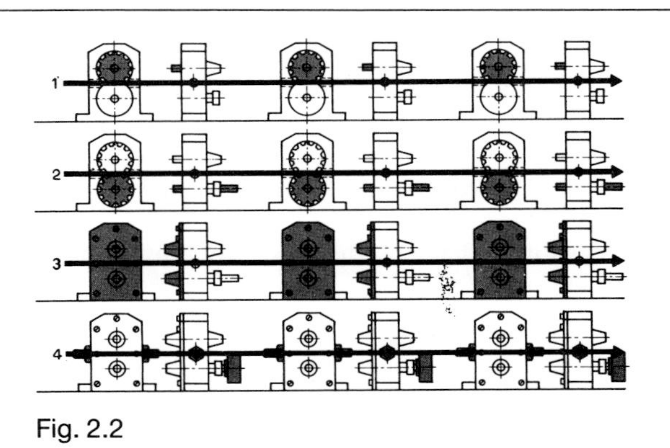

Fig. 2.2

5 An air compressor is to be installed in a factory. In addition to levelling and fastening it has to be aligned with an electric motor and existing pipe connection. This is an example of:
- a on site assembly
- b assembly line work
- c assembling trial erections
- d batch assembling

---

6 An example of mass production assembly line work is:
- a assembling a 30-section crane in a factory
- b building a batch of 30 identical pumps
- c building a motor car on a production line
- d assembling a large ocean liner

---

7 Consultation, pre-planning and the co-ordination of many assembly teams is essential when assembling which of the following?
- a large structures such as an off-shore drilling rig
- b the hydraulic system of a robot arm
- c a pistol drill
- d a 10-tonne s.w.l. jack

---

8 The pre-planning and consultations between assembly teams assembling the parts of a large chemical plant are necessary because without this:
- a not all the parts would be available
- b the assembly would be faulty on completion
- c the plant could not be completed efficiently in terms of manpower and parts
- d some of the parts would be lost

Refer to Fig. 2.3 in order to answer questions 9 and 10.

9 In order to test and modify the large crane, the manufacturers:
- a transport it to the site first and then complete the tests
- b test and modify each part as it comes off the production line
- c send for the government inspector to examine the parts
- d assemble the crane in the factory, dismantle it, then transport it to the work site

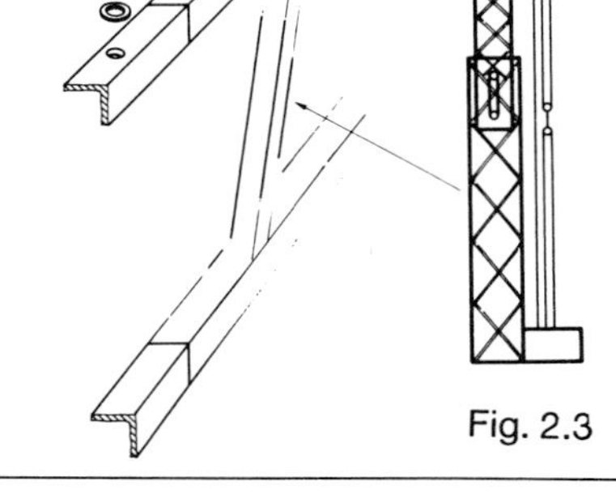

Fig. 2.3

---

10 To facilitate the re-erection of such large structures efficiently which of the following takes place?
- a the parts/joints are marked on a trial assembly
- b a set of power-assisted tools are used
- c the joints are painted with alternating colours
- d a test certificate of efficiency is issued

---

11 Refer to Fig. 2.4. If one of the pins projecting from the coupling was found to be broken off, 'on site' dismantling and repair of the coupling could best be achieved by:
- a welding the pin back to the flange face
- b leaving it till the opposite pin broke, thus halving the repair time
- c extracting the remains of the old pin and fitting a new one
- d riveting a piece of bar in until the coupling could be totally dismantled in the workshop

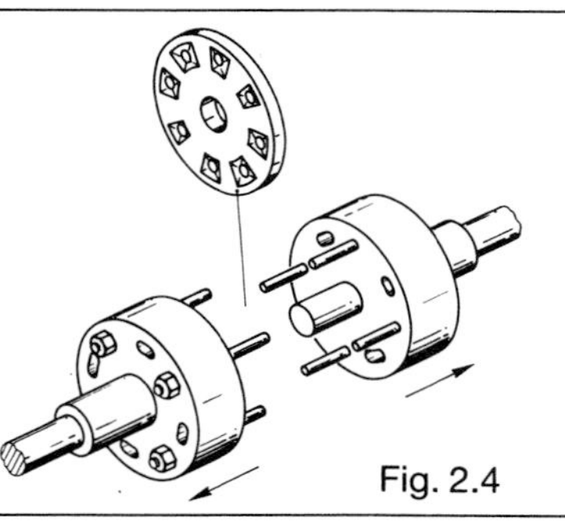

Fig. 2.4

12 On site dismantling prior to workshop repair is carried out because:
a there are more machines in the workshop
b repairs can be more conveniently and efficiently achieved in the workshop
c the assembly can be cleaned and inspected
d there are better tools in the workshop

13 Replacement at the work site of components, such as injector or burner nozzles, after which the faulty components are sent for workshop reconditioning, is the most efficient application of dismantling when:
a oxy-acetylene equipment is being used
b interruption of the working assembly is to be kept to a minimum
c petrol-fired engines are being serviced
d there is to be no interruption of the working assembly

In each of the following questions you are asked to explain the differences between a and b and give an example of each.

14 a partial fabrication, fitting and assembling on site

b assembling on site without pre-fabrication

15 a one off assembly

b assembling at an assembly line

16 a on site dismantling and repair

b on site replacement of components and workshop reconditioning of the replaced components

3 Selection of methods

The following questions relate to the above subject. Answers should be given as explained on page 75.

1 Component size must be considered when deciding upon a method of assembly because:
a lifting gear may be necessary
b safe practices may have to be worked out
c correct size tools must be available
d any combination of a, b and c

Refer to Fig. 3.1 in order to answer questions 2 and 3.

2 A hydraulic press is being used to assemble the 200 mm diameter bearing because:
a there is less friction on a hydraulic ram
b a smaller amount of force is required than when assembling the 20 mm diameter bearing
c a large amount of controlled force is required for the large diameter involved
d the shaft has clearance on the inner race

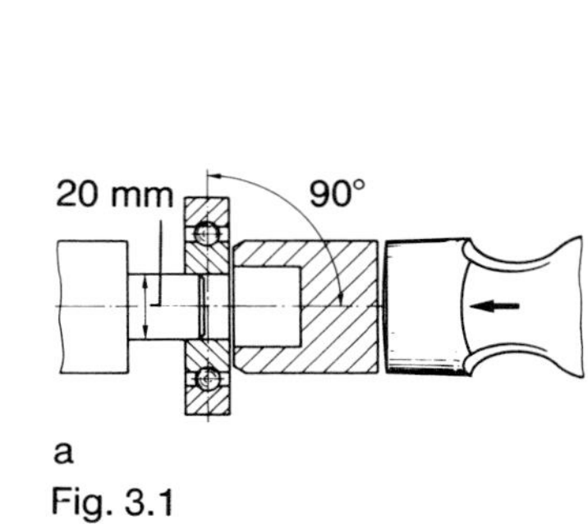

a

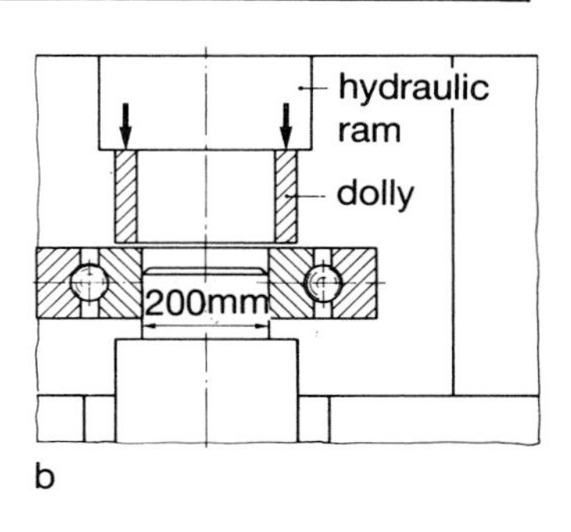

b

Fig. 3.1

3 Indicate which of the following is an example of a small assembly that can be assembled with hand tools on a workbench:

a crane
b lorry engine
c car engine piston and rings
d centre lathe, 600 mm swing

---

4 Large numbers of static parts are present in most structural assemblies. Failure to read drawings and follow construction planning sequences correctly can lead to:

a little or no difference in the time and money spent on the structure
b the whole structure being rebuilt
c unnecessary and time consuming dismantling and reassembly taking place
d all the parts being scrapped

Refer to Fig. 3.2 in order to answer questions 5 and 6.

5 The robot arm is an assembly with many moving parts. Failure to assemble the pistons and cylinders correctly could lead to:

a damage to the windscreen being fitted
b a pressure drop in the air supply
c sticking piston rings
d extra power on the suction lines

Fig. 3.2

6 If the piston and cylinders are correctly positioned but are fitted at random, i.e. not in the correct assembly sequence, then:

a the windscreen will be damaged
b subsequent dismantling and refitting of parts may have to be carried out
c the robot arm will be damaged
d there will be no difference to the amount of time needed to build the arm

---

7 Refer to Fig. 3.5. A component such as a trolley wheel will take a less exacting method of fitting than a plain bearing because:

a it is lubricated 'for life'
b the shell bearing is in one piece
c the component has a cotter fastener
d it is a more loosely toleranced component

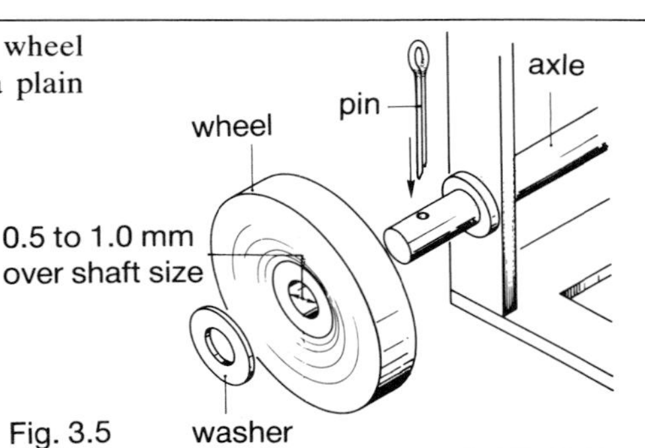

Fig. 3.5

---

8 a List FOUR factors about an assembly which could influence the method chosen to assemble it.
b Give reasons why the methods may vary when those factors are considered.

---

9 a List FOUR factors that may be taken into consideration when planning a method of dismantling an assembly.
b Give reasons why the methods of dismantling may vary when considering these factors.

---

4 Component relationships

The following questions relate to the above subject. Answers should be given as explained on page 75.

1 The purpose of the bolts shown in Fig. 4.1 is to:
- a load the coupling in tension
- b prevent movement of the coupling halves relative to each other
- c ensure the correct balance to the shaft
- d hold the drive keys in position

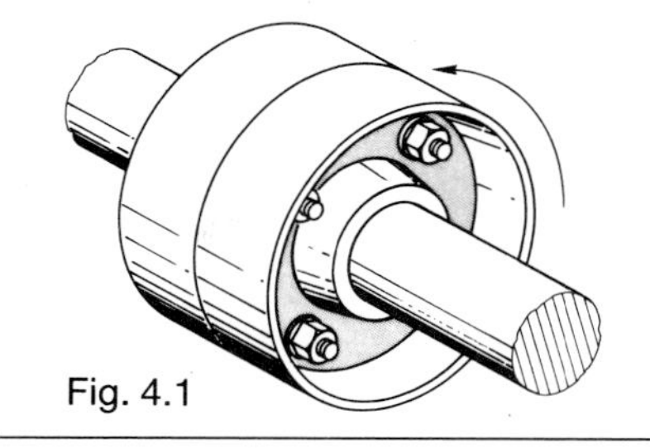

Fig. 4.1

2 The joint shown in Fig. 4.2:
- a is fluid tight but allows turning movement between parts
- b can be moved vertically without loss of fluid by using spring clips instead of bolts
- c allows reciprocating movement between parts whilst keeping the joint fluid tight
- d is fluid tight with no relative movements between parts

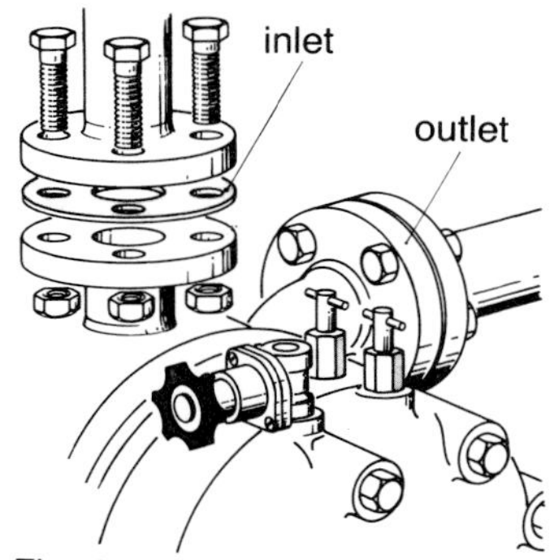

inlet
outlet

Fig. 4.2

3 In order to complete the assembly of the shaft connector in Fig. 4.3:
- a the moving part slides into the fixed part exactly
- b the parts must have a single tongue and groove
- c the fixed part can be at any angle relative to the moving part
- d the moving part must have a gib key

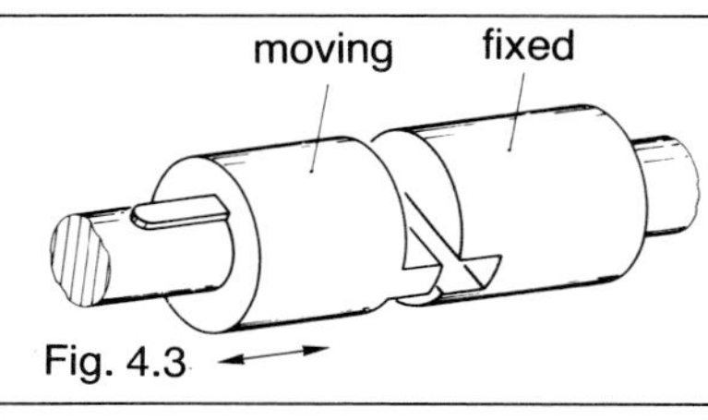

Fig. 4.3

4 The purpose of the seals on the piston shown in Fig. 4.4 is to enable:
- a the piston to slide and be fluid tight in relation to the cylinder
- b fluid to flow into the right-hand side of the cylinder
- c fluid to fill both sides of the cylinder at once
- d cylinder end caps to be lubricated

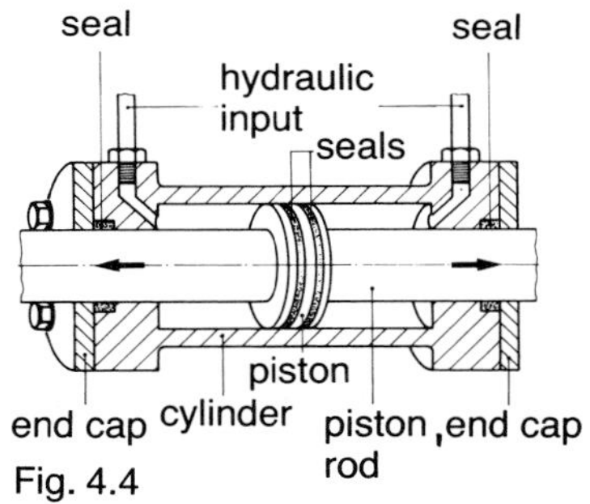

Fig. 4.4

5 The packing must be compressed on to the valve stem in Fig. 4.5 in order that:
- a it is not worn out too quickly
- b the stem is wedged in the safe position relative to the valve seat
- c the fluid is contained whilst the stem rotates
- d the rotary movement of the stem is in a clockwise direction

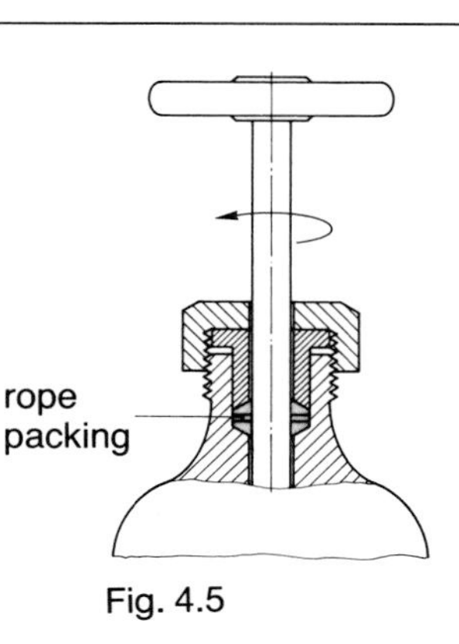

Fig. 4.5

6 After studying Fig. 4.6 complete the details in the table describing the relationship between the assembled components.

Neither component moves relative to the other	
One part rotates against the other	
	C
The joint between the non-moving parts is fluid tight	
The joint between the rotating and fixed components is fluid tight	

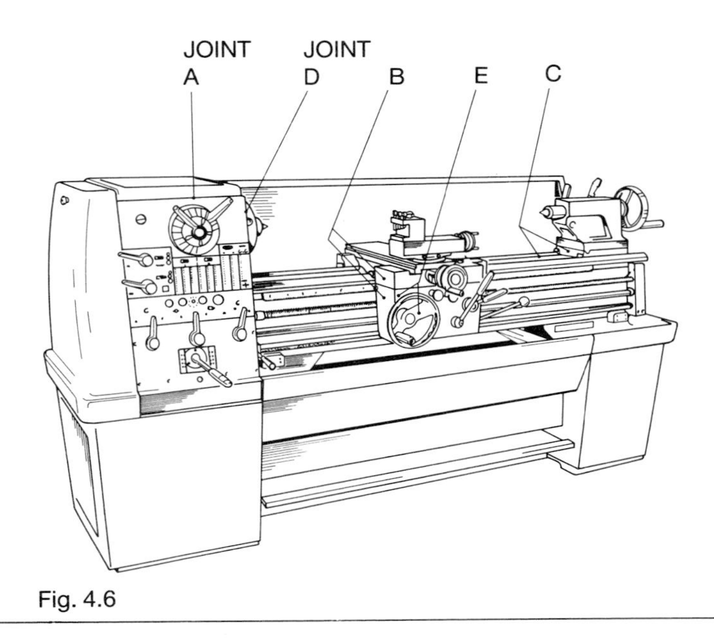

Fig. 4.6

5 Forces and their effects

The following questions relate to the above subject. Answers should be given as explained on page 75.

Refer to Fig. 5.1 in order to answer questions 1-3.

1 The force on the bolt shank indicated by the arrows in Fig. 5.1 is a:
a tensile force
b shear force
c compressive force
d torque force

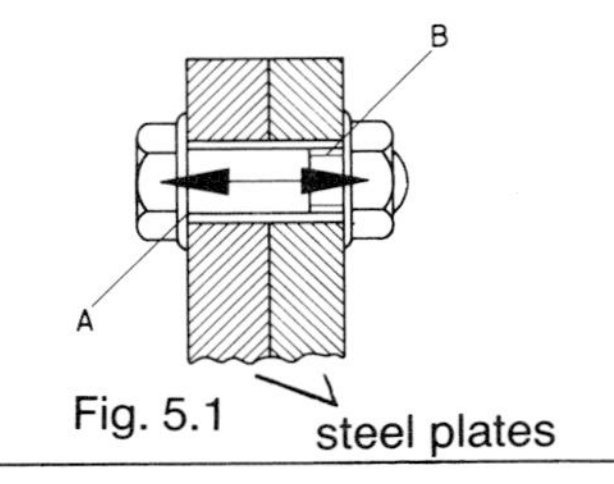

Fig. 5.1

2 The most likely result of an excessive force of the type indicated at Fig. 5.1 is:
a breakage of the tightening device
b breakage of the bolt at B
c excessive squeezing of the washers and plates
d breakage of the bolt at A

3 The steel plates in Fig. 5.1 are being subjected to:

- a a tensile load
- b a shear load
- c combined shear, tensile and compressive load
- d a compressive load

---

4 The roots of the threads of the bolt and nut at C and D (Fig. 5.2) are being subjected to a force that, if excessive across the lines indicated by the arrows, could break them. This load is described as:

- a compressive
- b tensile
- c shear
- d torque

Fig. 5.2

---

5 Complete the table below, in each case describing the type of force and its possible effects in the situation shown in Fig. 5.3 below.

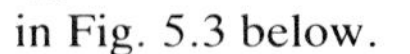

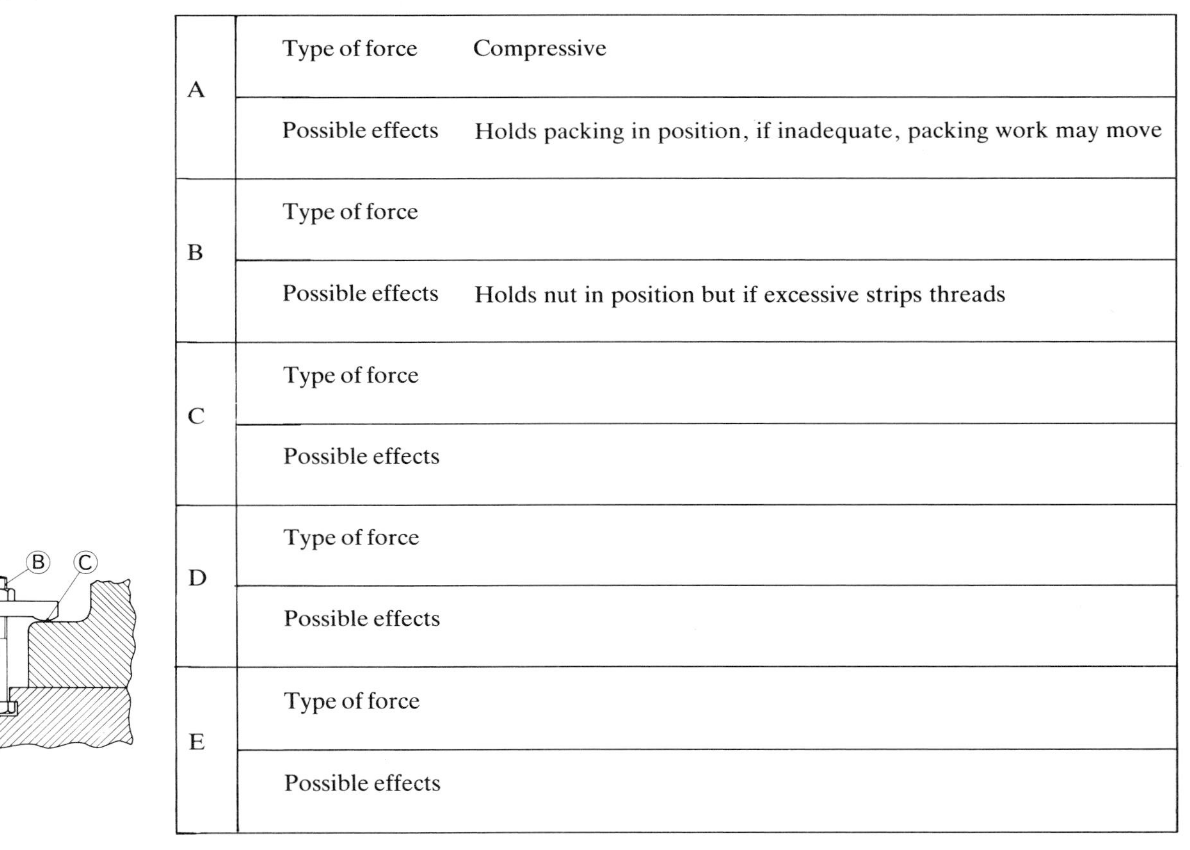

Fig. 5.3

A	Type of force	Compressive
	Possible effects	Holds packing in position, if inadequate, packing work may move
B	Type of force	
	Possible effects	Holds nut in position but if excessive strips threads
C	Type of force	
	Possible effects	
D	Type of force	
	Possible effects	
E	Type of force	
	Possible effects	

ASSEMBLING AND DISMANTLING Name: ______________________ Class: ________ Number: ____

6 Tools, form and principles

The following questions relate to the above subject. Answers should be given as explained on Page 75.

1	Rounded corners on the heads of bolts and on nuts are usually the result of using:	a b c d	a spanner with excessive clearance between nut and jaws too great a force whilst tightening an impact spanner a long handled single-ended ring spanner
2	The jaws of an open-ended spanner are set at an angle to the body because:	a b c d	they are most easily manufactured in this shape in restricted situations they allow the spanner to be turned over, thus facilitating greater manipulation it makes spanner storage more convenient they slide more easily on to the nut
3	Ring spanners and socket wrenches are used when access to the nut is:	a b c d	possible from the top only not in a confined space in a confined space possible from the side only
4	An advantage of using a ring spanner or socket wrench instead of an open-ended spanner is that either of them	a b c d	is stronger can be used in confined spaces can be used with a pipe to increase handle length is less likely to slip when force is applied
5	When a hexagon socket spanner is used for finally tightening a set-screw:	a b c d	the long leg is inserted into the socket to ensure that more tightening force can be applied the long leg is inserted into the socket to ensure that the exact tightening force can be applied the short leg is inserted into the socket to ensure that the tightening force is not exceeded the short leg is inserted into the socket to ensure that the correct tightening force can be applied
6	Impact wrenches are often used where:	a b c d	the nuts or bolts have to be broken to be dismantled an ordinary spanner slips off the sudden force of the blow releases the bolt or nut more easily than the sustained force at the end of a normal spanner of the same size a ratchet spanner will not shake the bolt or nut sufficiently to loosen it
7	On inspection the corners of a bolt head are found to be rounded. Use of which of the following tools is the possible cause?	a b c d	a ring spanner with an internal dodecagon shaped head an adjustable spanner which has not been correctly adjusted to bolt head size a spanner made from a material harder than that of the bolt head an open-ended spanner with a sliding fit over the bolt head
8	Water pump pliers, stilsons and chain wrenches are all types of:	a b c d	pliers chain adjusters non adjustable pipe spanners pipe wrenches
9	Stilson jaws bite into the component, thus preventing slippage whilst tightening. This is because they are:	a b c d	specially hardened specially shaped and hardened flat and hard shaped to the exact size of the component

10 Refer to Fig. 6.1. The blade of the screwdriver is grooved as indicated so as to:
- a help prevent slippage when the screw is tightened or slackened
- b make it easier to enter the slot of the screw
- c help prevent slippage when the screw is tightened
- d make it easier to see if the blade is centrally aligned in the slot when tightening or slackening the screw

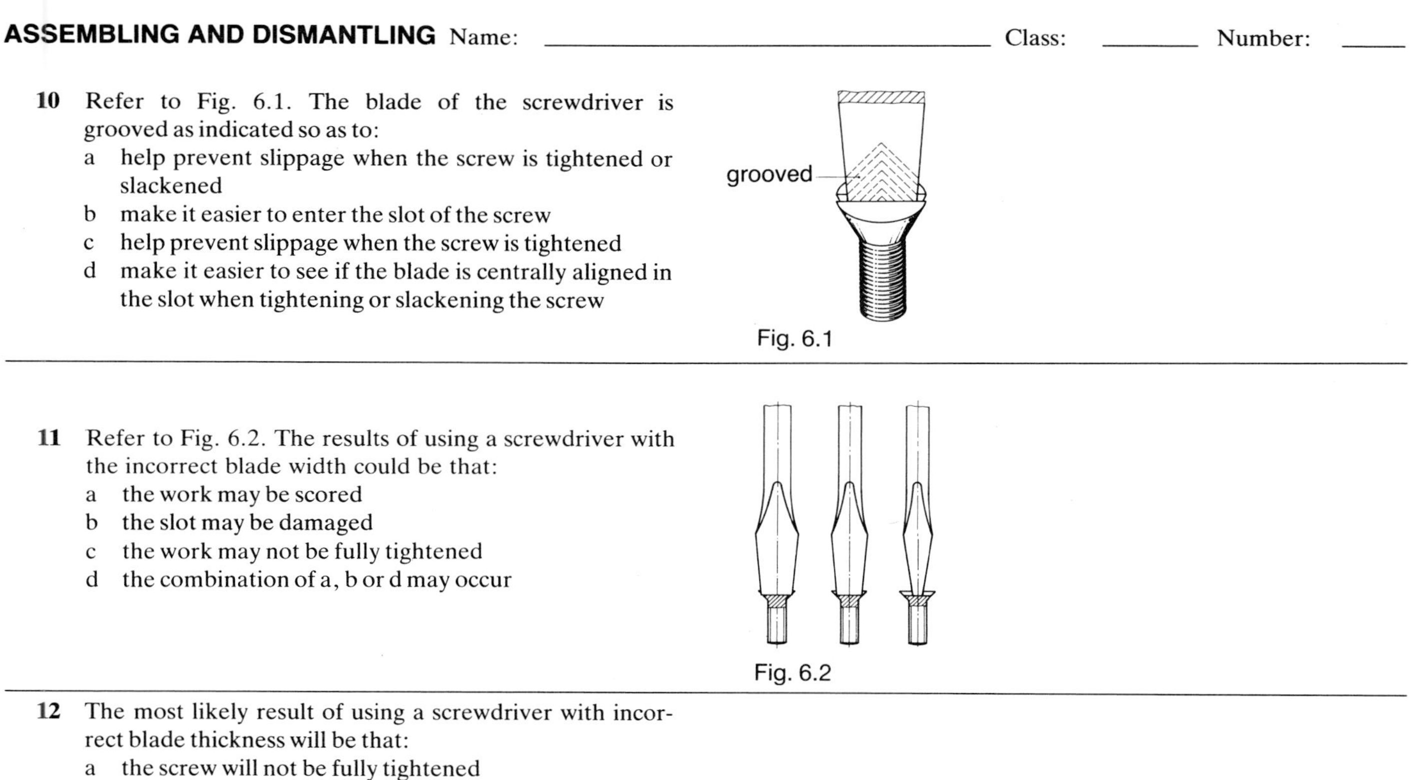

Fig. 6.1

---

11 Refer to Fig. 6.2. The results of using a screwdriver with the incorrect blade width could be that:
- a the work may be scored
- b the slot may be damaged
- c the work may not be fully tightened
- d the combination of a, b or d may occur

Fig. 6.2

---

12 The most likely result of using a screwdriver with incorrect blade thickness will be that:
- a the screw will not be fully tightened
- b the work will be damaged
- c the blade tip will break off
- d the sides of the slot will be damaged

---

13 Refer to Fig. 6.3. The long-nosed pliers shown are shaped that way because:
- a this gives them better shearing leverage
- b they are cheaper to produce
- c this gives them more grip for twisting wire
- d manipulation in confined spaces is easier

Fig. 6.3

---

14 A large amount of force is available at the jaws of pliers by the application of an important principle. It is described as the principle of:
- a levers
- b moments
- c shear force
- d twisting force

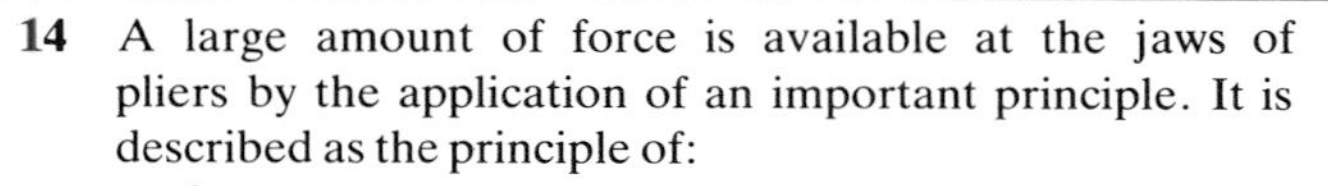

---

15 A hammer has to be used whilst assembling a cast aluminium gearbox housing. The hammer shown in Fig. 6.4 is chosen because:
- a it offers a choice of two different materials on the faces
- b the head has replaceable parts
- c it has soft faces and will not damage the work
- d the shaft is stocky and will withstand impact well

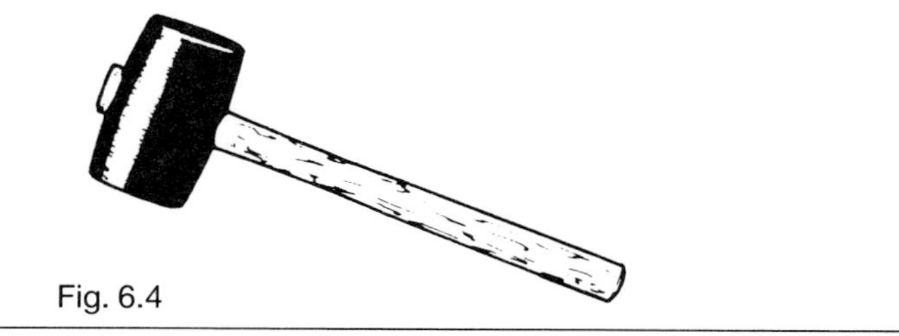

Fig. 6.4

---

16 A packing has to be made which will fit between two flanges on a water pipe. The hammer shown in Fig. 6.5 is chosen because:
- a it has a hard flat face
- b the ball pein will cut internal radii
- c the head has a cross and a straight pane
- d it will not cut the packing

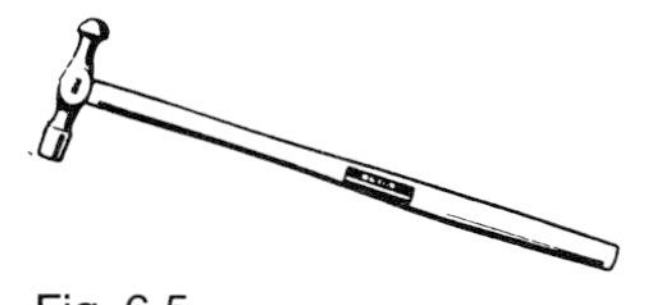

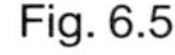

Fig. 6.5

17 Pin punches such as those shown in Fig. 6.6, when used with the appropriate size and shape of hammer, are better for pin extraction than mild steel bars of similar size because they:
- a are more expensive
- b are made from hardened and tempered steel so they will not bend
- c use the leverage principle, making extraction easier
- d are tapered, so that clearance is obtained behind the pin

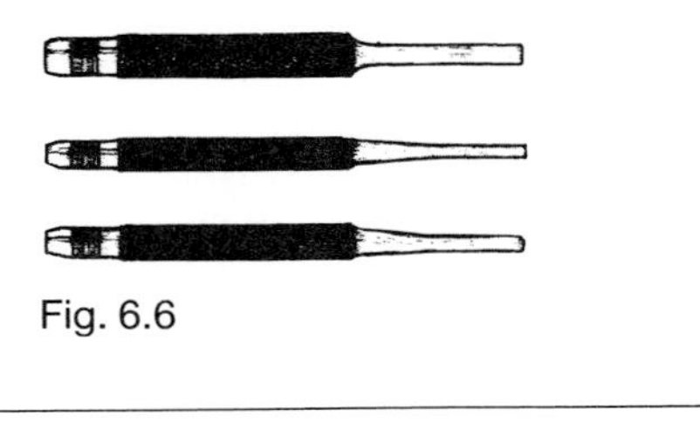
Fig. 6.6

18 The 'jumbo' key extractor shown in Fig. 6.7 is a type of:
- a lever
- b key spanner
- c wedge extractor
- d key punch

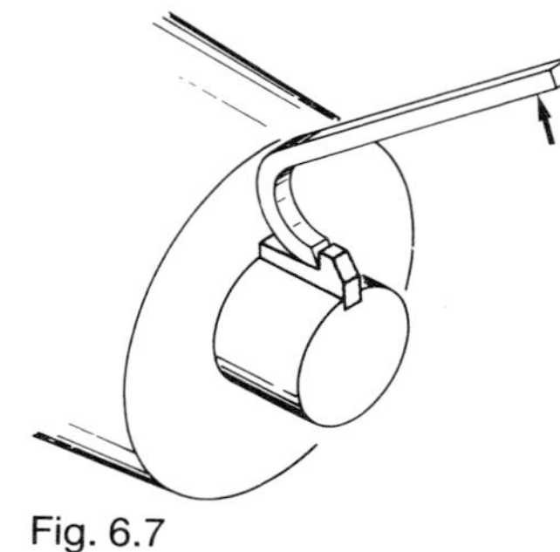
Fig. 6.7

19 The combined podger bar and ring spanner shown in Fig. 6.8 is most likely to be used when:
- a fitting the top of a gear box where the gear box has studs
- b tightening screws when extra leverage can be obtained by slipping a pipe over the podger
- c cleaning out the recesses of sunken bolt heads with the podger before tightening with the ring end is achieved
- d aligning holes in girders before fitting and tightening bolts

Fig. 6.8

20 A suitable piece of equipment for the initial lift of the machine shown in Fig. 6.9 is:
- a a screw jack
- b a hydraulic jack
- c a crow bar
- d a lever jack

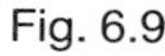
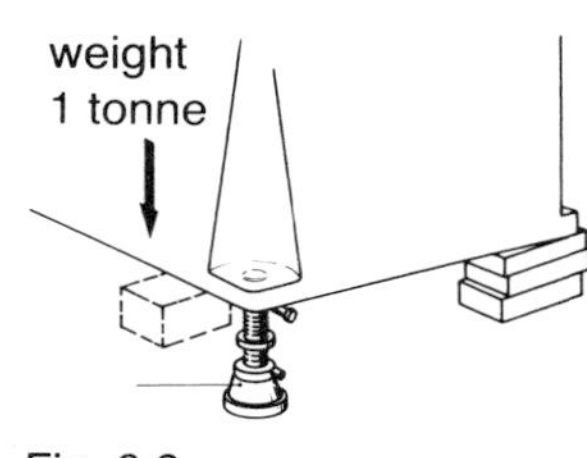

Fig. 6.9

21 The initials S.W.L. stamped on the sides of jacks stand for:
- a safe working load
- b safe weight leverage
- c straight weight lift
- d secondary working load

22 The S.W.L. of a jack must not be exceeded because:
- a it could lead to lifting the machine too high
- b the jack may fail, causing injury to the operator and damage to the work being lifted
- c the jack handle will break, causing extensive damage
- d the hydraulic oil will leak, causing the wet floor to be a safety hazard

Give short and clear answers to the following questions.

23 Explain how torque is controlled on the types of assembly tool listed below:
- a open-ended spanner
- b torque spanner
- c screwdriver

24
- a Name the type of tool that can be set at a given torque value.
- b Give an application where torque control is an essential requirement when assembling.

25 State reasons why correct selection and application of the following tools are important:
- a open-ended spanners
- b flat blade screwdrivers
- c crow bars

7 Purpose of tools and devices used

The following questions relate to the above subject. Answers should be given as explained on page 75.

Refer to Figs. 7.1 and 7.2 to help you answer questions 1 and 2.

1 Studs:
- a need a long nut at one end and a short nut at the other in order to fasten the components together in an assembly
- b are only used in an assembly where bolt and set-screw heads will not fit
- c are usually taken out of the assembly when dismantling takes place
- d are fitted by the short thread into one part of the assembly before further assembling takes place

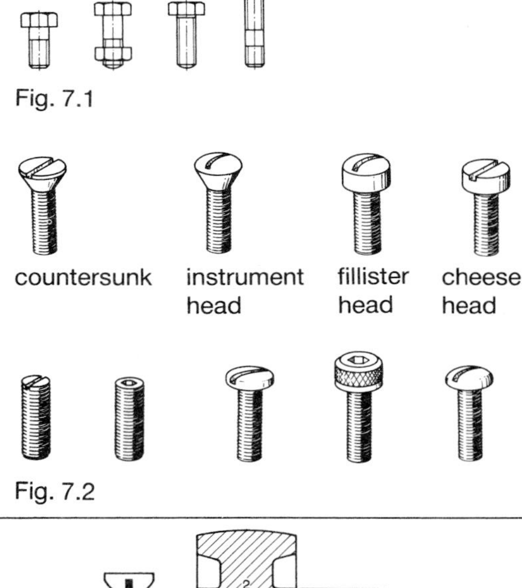

Fig. 7.1

Fig. 7.2

2 The head of a countersunk headed screw is:
- a usually protruding above the joint surface
- b always below the joint surface when in the tightened position
- c fitted into a counterbored hole and flush with the joint surface
- d tightened on to a shakeproof washer to stop it unscrewing

Refer to Fig. 7.3 in order to answer questions 3 and 4.

3 The best alternative screw for that shown in Fig. 7.3 is a:
- a cap headed screw
- b countersunk headed screw
- c socketed grub screw
- d hexagon headed screw

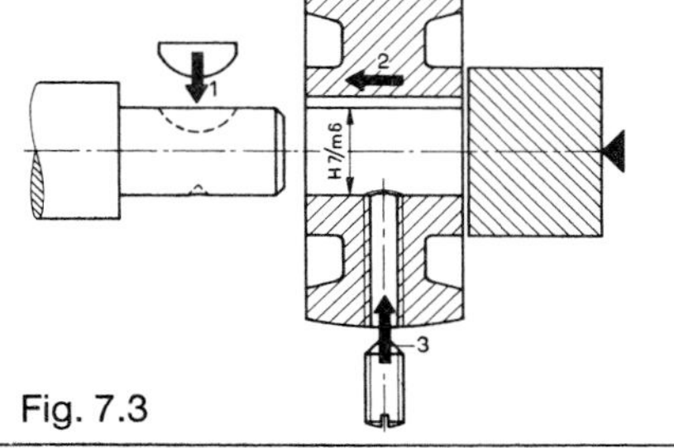

Fig. 7.3

4 The best alternative way of fastening and locating the pulley to the shaft in Fig. 7.3 would be to use:

a only a feather key
b only a woodruff key
c only a gib headed taper key
d a taper key and grub screw

---

5 Precise relocation and fastening of components such as hand-wheels on shafts can best be achieved by using

a pins
b bolts
c precision studs
d cotter washers

---

6 A hollow spring pin will achieve the same results as a parallel pin but offers the advantage that it:

a is a tighter fit
b does not need oiling on assembly
c will retain oil and therefore not rust
d does not require a reamed hole

Refer to Fig. 7.4 in order to answer questions 7 and 8.

7 To be suitable for securing the brake pads to the pivot arms an adhesive should:

a adhere to both pivot arm and brake pad and resist high pressures and temperatures
b be able to resist water
c have high strength and be water, oil and chemical resistant
d adhere to both pivot arm and brake pad at low temperatures

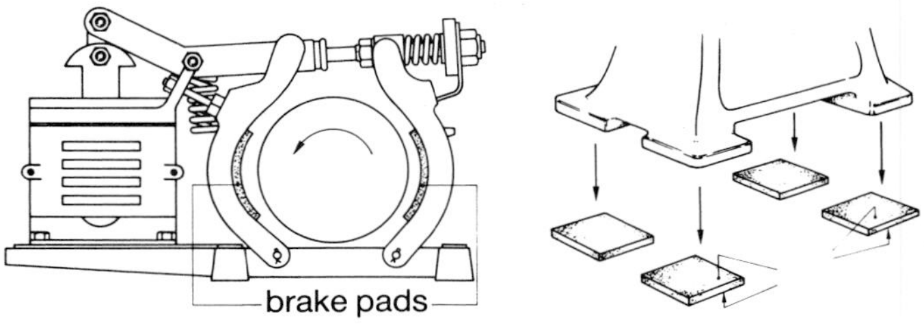

brake pads

Fig. 7.4

---

8 An adhesive that would be most suited to secure the machine to the floor should:

a be able to resist water and high temperatures
b be an epoxy resin
c have high strength and be water, oil and chemical resistant
d be permanent so that the pads cannot be parted from the machine

---

9 For an adhesive to be an effective jointing material the surfaces that are to accept the adhesives must:

a be shot blasted
b be chemically clean
c be smooth
d be rough

---

10 A stud in the moving part of an engine assembly was found to have worked loose in service. On replacement to prevent it from falling out and causing damage, the stud:

a was replaced by a bolt and nut with a locking device
b was held in position by the appropriate adhesive
c had a lock nut fitted
d was welded in position

Refer to Fig. 7.5 to answer questions 11-14.

11 The type of locking device that incorporates the use of a split pin is a:

a lock nut
b self-locking nut
c tab washer
d castle nut

---

12 A type of locking device that relies totally on friction for its locking action is a:

a slotted nut
b tab washer
c castle nut
d lock nut

---

13 A type of locking device that relies upon a positive stop for its locking action is a:

a nut with a plastic insert
b nut with a depitched turret
c slotted nut
d lock nut

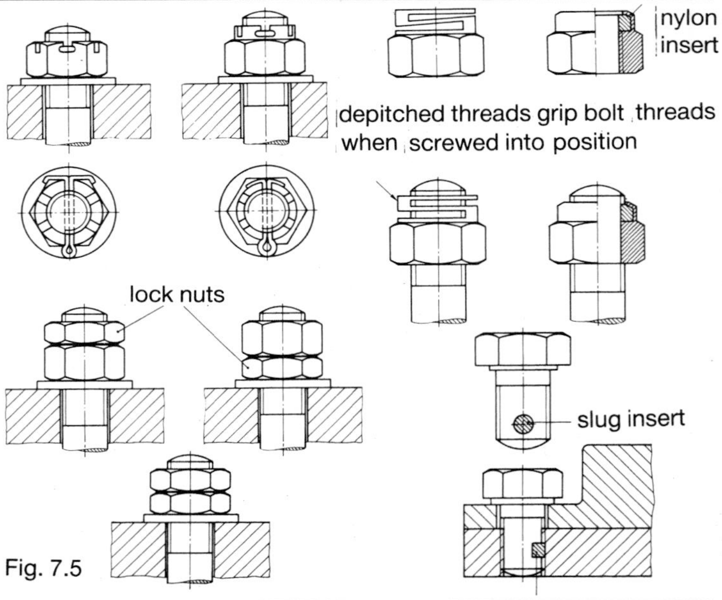

nylon insert

depitched threads grip bolt threads when screwed into position

lock nuts

slug insert

Fig. 7.5

14 Positive stop locking devices are more expensive to fit than are those relying on friction, but under normal circumstances they can be expected to:

a be totally reliable in the locked position
b hold the component tighter
c be stronger and longer-lasting
d stop stud fittings from shaking loose

---

15 A typical application of a positive locking device is on the:

a bolts of a coupling
b studs securing a rocker valve cover
c flange adjusting nuts
d crankshaft bearing nuts

---

16 Sealing devices are used in assemblies to:

a prevent gas or fluid leakage
b fill in surface cracks and so prevent breakage
c make joints adhere to each other
d fill in holes and therefore prevent component loss

---

17 Refer to Figs. 7.6 – 7.8 to answer this question.
All gaskets. 'O' rings and gland packings are:

a made from synthetic rubber
b circular
c sealing devices
d made from either cork or asbestos fibre

---

18 The material chosen for the gasket in Fig. 7.6 will be:

a cork, because this is the cheapest material for a gasket seal
b a material suitable for the mating materials, the pressure, temperature and nature of process materials involved
c a material suitable for the size of the joint
d a synthetic rubber and cork mixture, because it needs to be waterproof

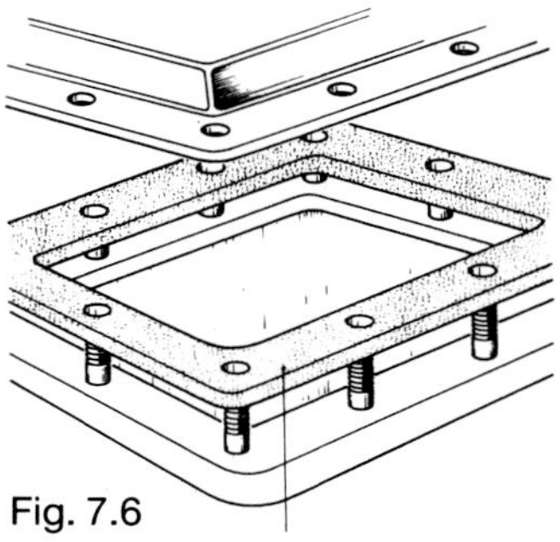

Fig. 7.6

---

19 The lip seal shown in Fig. 7.7.

a rotates with the bearing, thus sealing the end in
b relies on rotation and spring pressure to keep the oil in
c stops oil leakage from the bearing area and contamination entering the bearing area from outside
d is a type of rigid mechanical seal

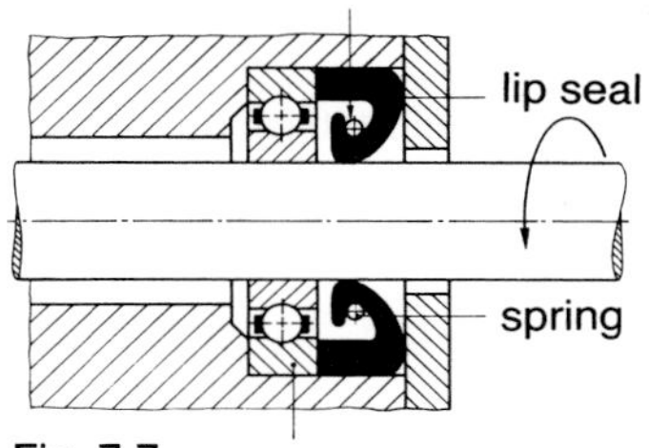

lip seal
spring

Fig. 7.7

---

20 Fig. 7.8 shows 'o' rings used as moving seals on a pneumatic spool valve. Whilst assembling such seals, care must be taken to:

a heat the seals to the right expansion temperature
b get them the correct way round
c hold the ring open with pliers
d prevent damage to their surface

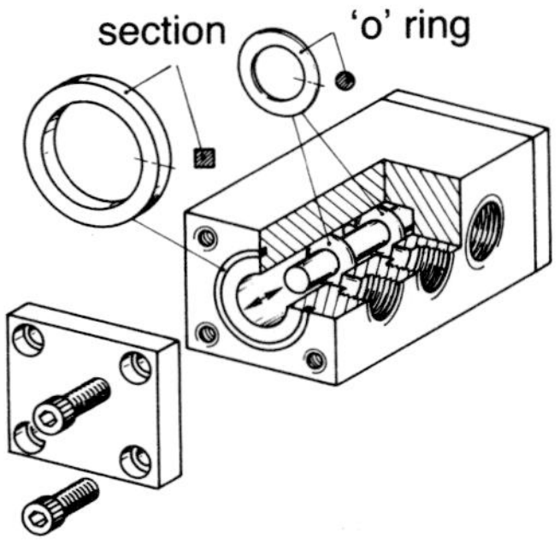

section
'o' ring

Fig. 7.8

---

21 When a bearing is being shrunk on to a shaft, gloves and goggles should be worn, because:

a an oil bath is being used to heat the bearing
b an induction coil is being used to heat the bearing
c a refrigerator is being used to cool the bearing
d dry ice is being used to cool the bearing

---

22 Fig. 7.9 shows a bearing being cooled by the dry ice method. When the bearing has reached the correct temperature it can be positioned:

a on the shaft, so that on expansion there will be an interference fit between it and the shaft
b on the shaft, so that on contraction there will be a clearance fit between it and the shaft
c into the housing, so that on expansion there will be a clearance fit between it and the housing
d into the housing, so that on expansion there will be an interference fit between it and the housing

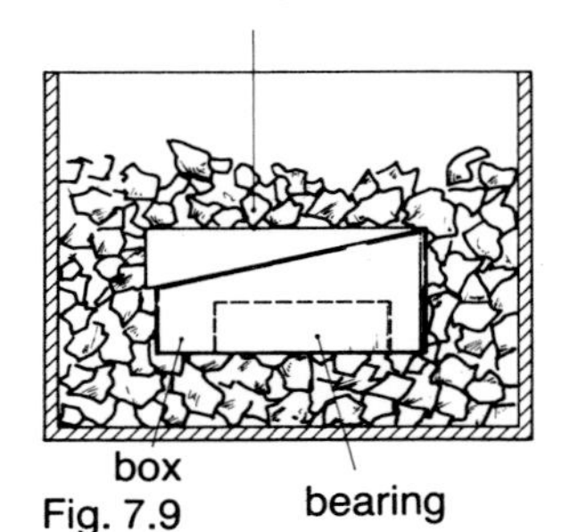

Fig. 7.9

---

23 A 100 mm diameter bearing is to be fitted on to a shaft. The resistance of the interference fits encountered can be overcome safely whilst maintaining accurate position of the bearing by:

a carefully hammering alternate sides of the bearing with a ball pein hammer
b placing a soft metal tube over the outer raceway and hitting it with a percussive instrument
c using a hydraulic press
d carefully hammering alternate sides of the bearing with a copper-faced hammer

---

24 Fig. 7.10 shows a bearing being pushed from its housing with the aid of a press. The housing is being supported by packings and:

a the packings are forcing the housing up over the bearing in a vertical direction
b the dolly is being pressed on the outer race only, so that no damage is done to balls or raceways
c all the pressure of the press is being directed down the centre line
d the downward force is being absorbed by the inner raceway

Fig. 7.10

Refer to Fig. 7.11 to answer questions 25 to 32.

25 The best type of equipment used to establish the horizontal datum of a centre lathe would be a:

a plumb line
b precision spirit level
c clinometer
d barometer

---

26 The best type of equipment to establish a vertical datum whilst erecting a steel girder would be a:

a plumb line
b clinometer
c precision spirit level
d protractor

---

27 On a machine tool such as a milling machine, the vertical datum or column can be most accurately checked by the use of a:

a protractor with a vernier attachment
b plumb line
c vernier height gauge
d box level

---

28 The amount of clearance or 'backlash' between mating gear teeth can be checked most easily by using a:

a straight edge
b set of slip gauges
c dial test indicator
d set of feeler gauges

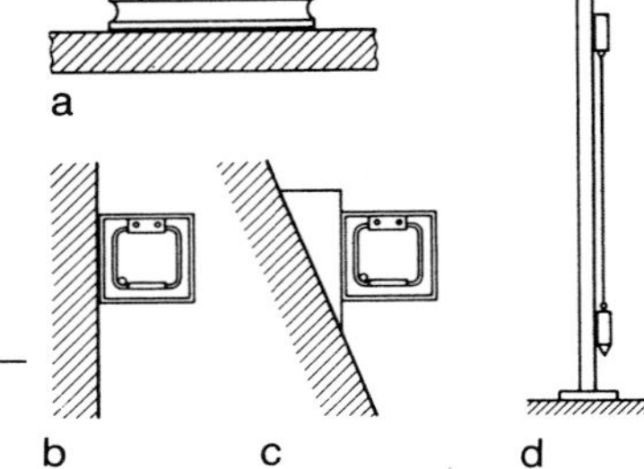

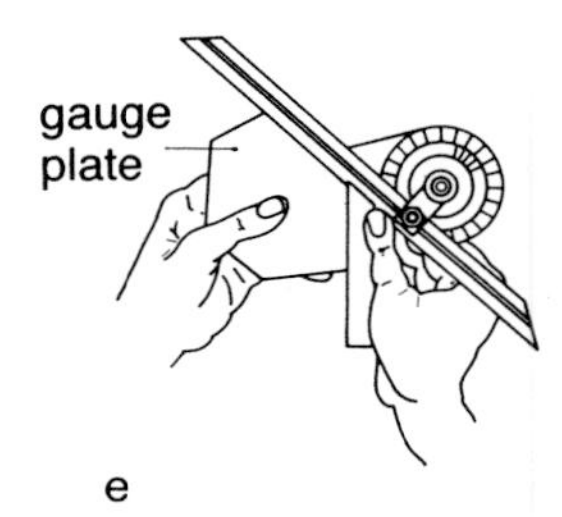

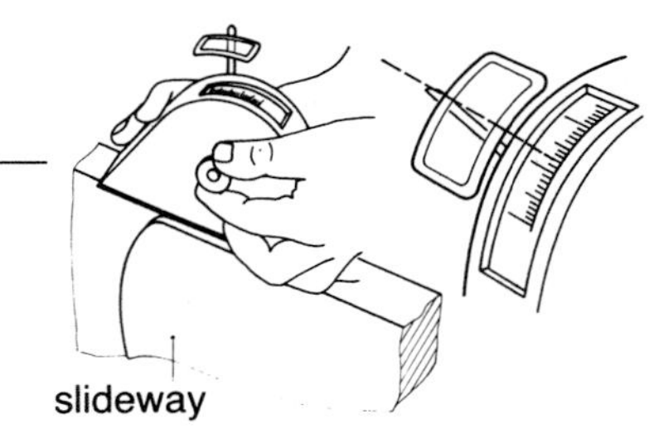

g

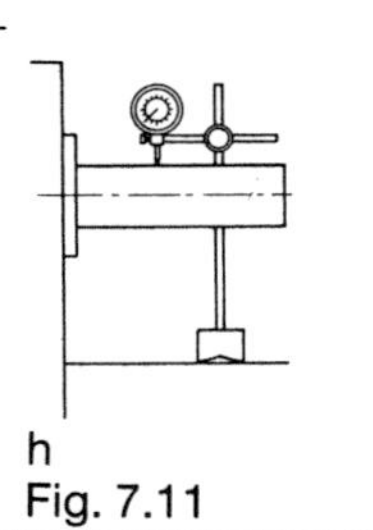

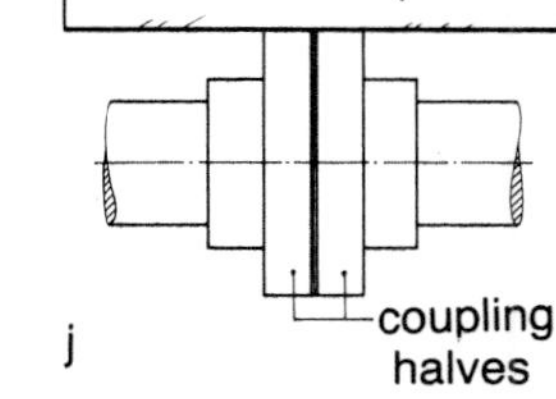

Fig. 7.11

---

29 A test bar is inserted into the spindle of a vertical milling machine and then revolved against a dial test indicator placed on the table. The amount of movement registered on the dial indicates:
a surface errors
b vertical alignment errors
c horizontal alignment errors
d concentricity errors

30 The coupling halves are being checked for alignment and position with the axis of the shaft. For correct alignment and position to be ascertained the straight edge should be placed:
a on top of the couplings
b at 90° to the first place tested
c along both sides of the coupling
d at 180° to the first place tested

31 When no light can be seen between the straight edge and the two coupling halves:
a a straight line has been established
b angular misalignment is present
c axial misalignment is present
d a flat surface has been established

32 The most suitable equipment for establishing both axial and angular alignments of coupling halves is:
a a dial test indicator and stand with slip gauges
b a vernier protractor and straight edge
c a straight edge and vernier caliper
d feeler gauges and a straight edge

33 Fig. 7.12 illustrates a cleaning and storage sequence for assembly parts. After treatment with white spirit the parts are:
a left with an invisible protective spirit coating and ready for storage
b ready for a final clean in light oil
c chemically clean and dry, and ready for inspection for wear or damage
d heated to dry off the white spirit, ready for final cleaning in light oil

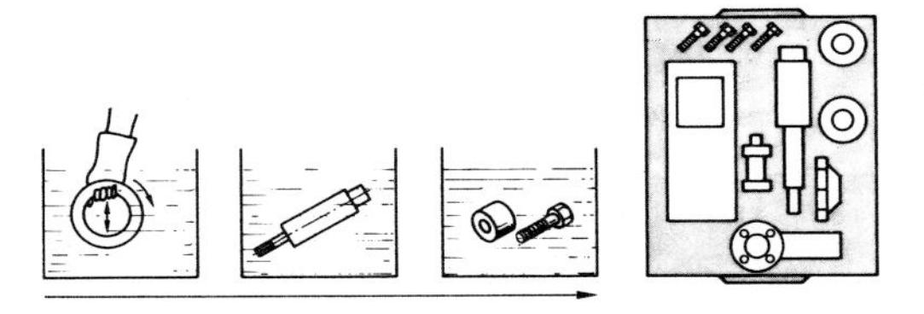

Fig. 7.12

34 When carbon tetrachloride is used to degrease components, adequate ventilation is required because:
a there is a danger of asphixiation
b the components will need to dry off quickly
c there is extra heat generated by the process
d there is a danger of fire

35 Acid baths should not be used in the cleaning of copper because of the danger that:
a the parts may fuse together
b the chemical reaction may form a toxic gas
c there may be an explosion
d the acid may seriously damage the component

36 Caustic soda baths should not be used in the cleaning of light alloys because of the danger that:
a the parts may fuse together
b the caustic soda may seriously damage the component
c the chemical reaction may form a toxic gas
d there may be an explosion

37 For protection of the hands against oils, dirt and grease:
- a barrier cream should be applied before work begins
- b cotton gloves should be worn
- c the hands should be washed at regular intervals
- d leather gloves should be worn

---

38 Fig. 7.13 shows a universal joint and shaft assembly. After strip down, cleaning, and inspection, the shaft must be reassembled in strict sequence by matching the marks, because otherwise it:
- a may be impossible to assemble
- b may not rotate
- c is likely to shudder and vibrate when revolving as a result of being out of balance
- d is likely to prove very difficult to dismantle again

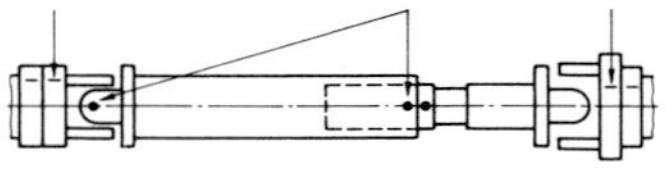

reassembly lines location marks reassembly marks

Fig. 7.13

---

39 If there are six bearings in line, each similar to the one in Fig. 7.14, it is essential to pair the numbers and realign the marks on reassembly because:
- a these are interchangeable assembly parts
- b the tops will not fit in any other position
- c each bearing has been individually scraped to suit the shaft at that position
- d the securing bolts will only fit in when the marks align

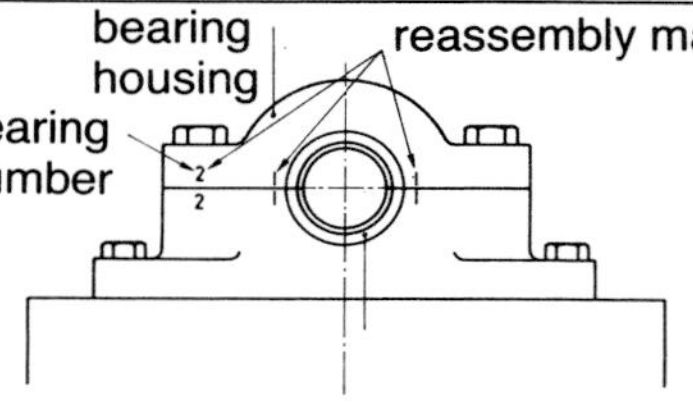

bearing housing reassembly marks bearing number

Fig. 7.14

---

40 If a component such as a bolt or pulley is rusted to an assembly and will not separate by normal methods, usually the first treatment used to aid dismantling is to:
- a apply penetrating oil to the joint surfaces
- b apply a hydraulic pulley drawer
- c try a bolt extractor
- d coat the surfaces with oil

---

41 Refer to Fig. 7.15. The best way of removing a stud which has broken off flush with the casting into which it is screwed is to:
- a apply the device shown in Fig. 7.15a
- b use the device shown in Fig. 7.15c
- c burn it out
- d apply the device shown in Fig. 7.15b

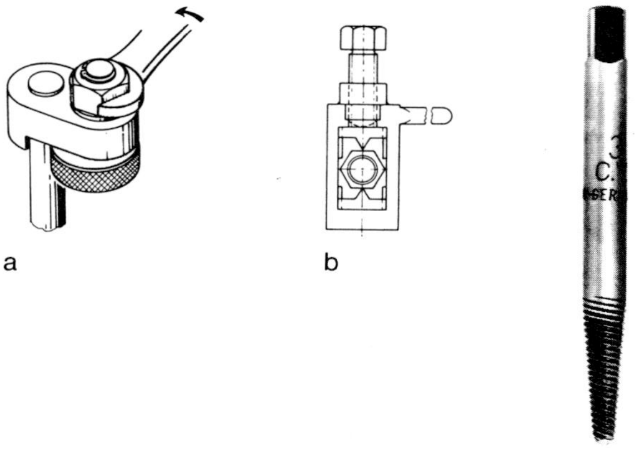

a b c

Fig. 7.15

---

42 To remove the timing chain cover shown in Fig. 7.16 (on a machine having very critical timing) requires:
- a a socket wrench
- b a special purpose tool
- c a pentagonal open-ended spanner
- d an adjustable spanner

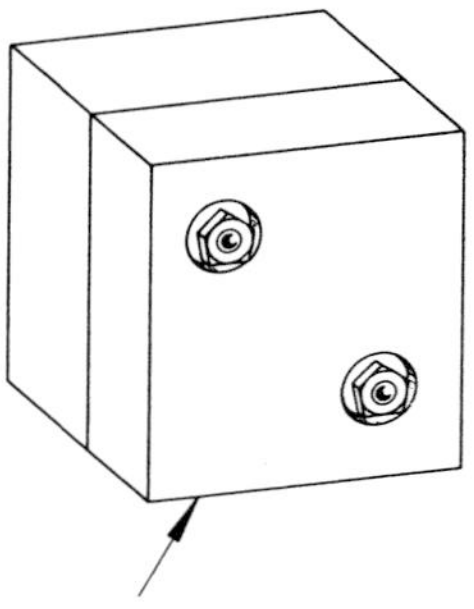

timing chain cover

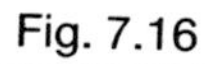

Fig. 7.16

43 The reason for the use of such a tool in question 42 is that:
- a other types of spanners are not strong enough
- b a specified torque is required on the nut
- c this will make it difficult for unauthorised entry to the box
- d hexagon nuts are not strong enough

44 So that a bearing can be removed from a shaft easily and not suffer damage:
- a pressure is applied to the outer raceway only
- b the shaft is injected with penetrating oil
- c pressure is applied to any part of the bottom of the bearing
- d pressure is applied to the inner raceway only

45 In order to distribute more evenly the force available for drawing off pulleys and bearings from shafts a:
- a hydraulic pulley drawer is used
- b three-legged pulley drawer is used
- c two-legged pulley drawer is used
- d combined pulley drawer and bearing splitter is used

46 Usually a three-legged puller is employed when dismantling large assemblies (such as flywheels) because:
- a the puller legs are cranked to reach behind the flywheel
- b the flywheel is less likely to 'cant' and stick
- c such pullers are hydraulically operated
- d the flywheel is fitted with three slots to accommodate the puller legs

47 It is found necessary to use heat to loosen the flywheel shown in Fig. 7.17 before attempting to pull it from the boss. The heat should be applied:
- a evenly around the centre of the flywheel boss, so that distortion or cracking does not occur
- b to the shaft only, so that the flywheel is not damaged
- c to the compressor boss, so that on expansion it will push off the flywheel
- d to the rim of the flywheel, therefore keeping distortion to a minimum

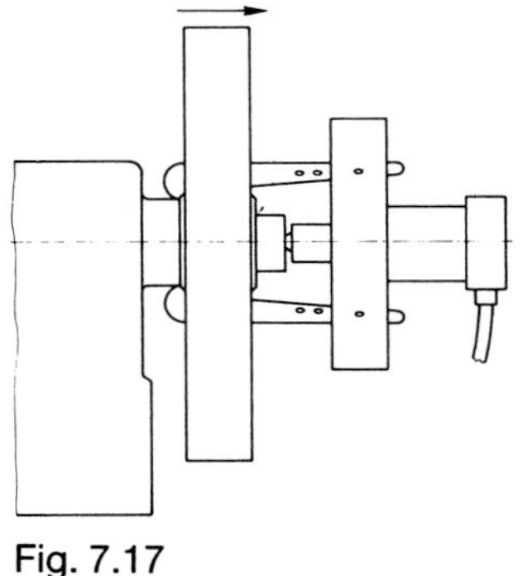

Fig. 7.17

48 Where heat is applied to crack joints, distortion of adjacent parts can best be kept to a minimum by using carefully distributed:
- a thermo jackets
- b ice packs
- c thermocouples
- d heat shields

49 Explain the difference between, and quote examples of the use of:
- a bolts and set-screws
- b taper and parallel pins
- c positive and frictional locking devices
- d stationary and moving seals

50 Describe the purpose of the following devices when used for dismantling purposes:
- a cleaning agents
- b penetrating oils
- c gear pullers
- d presses

8 Precautions to be taken

The following questions relate to the above subject. Answers should be given as explained on page 75.

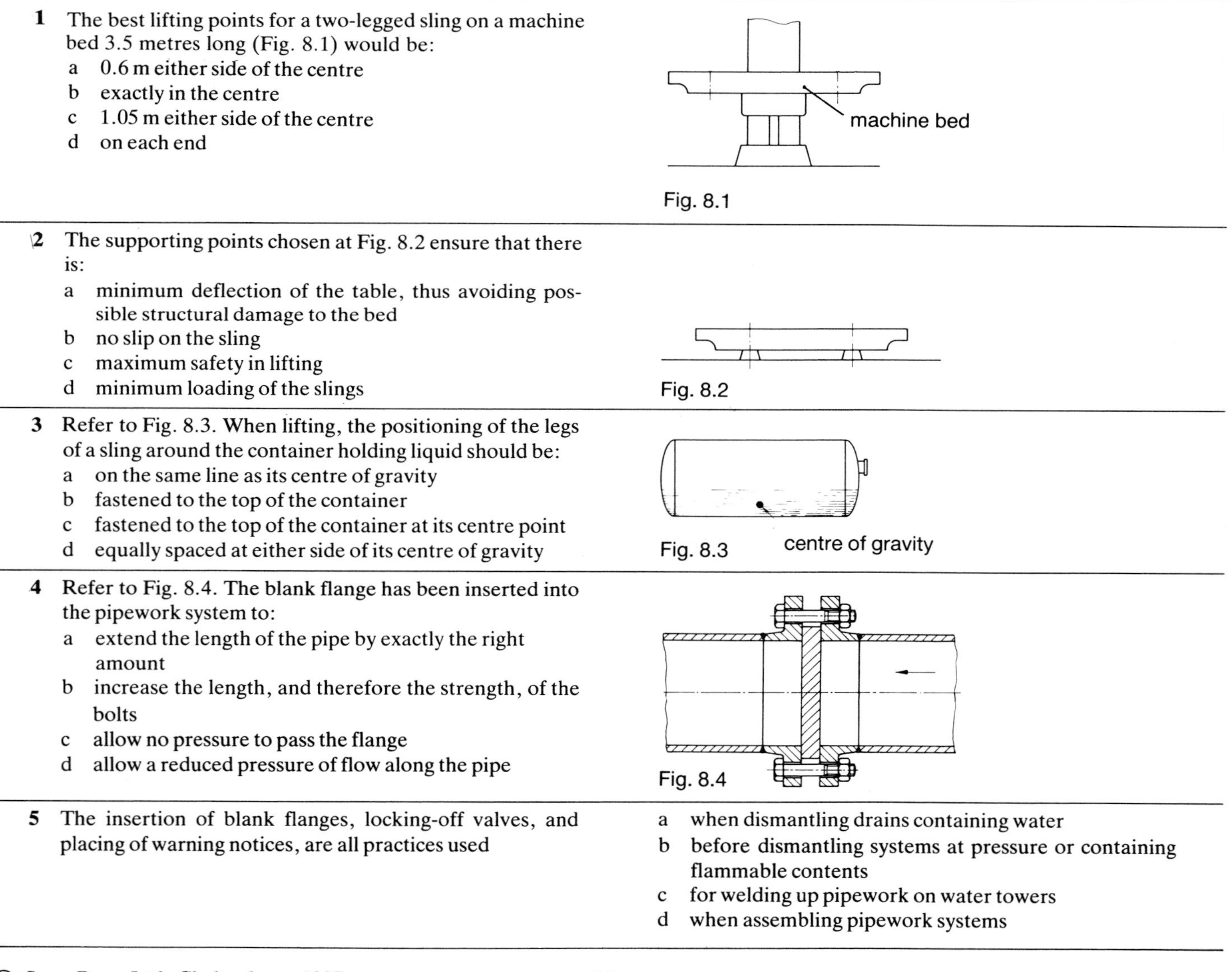

1 The best lifting points for a two-legged sling on a machine bed 3.5 metres long (Fig. 8.1) would be:
- a 0.6 m either side of the centre
- b exactly in the centre
- c 1.05 m either side of the centre
- d on each end

Fig. 8.1

2 The supporting points chosen at Fig. 8.2 ensure that there is:
- a minimum deflection of the table, thus avoiding possible structural damage to the bed
- b no slip on the sling
- c maximum safety in lifting
- d minimum loading of the slings

Fig. 8.2

3 Refer to Fig. 8.3. When lifting, the positioning of the legs of a sling around the container holding liquid should be:
- a on the same line as its centre of gravity
- b fastened to the top of the container
- c fastened to the top of the container at its centre point
- d equally spaced at either side of its centre of gravity

Fig. 8.3

4 Refer to Fig. 8.4. The blank flange has been inserted into the pipework system to:
- a extend the length of the pipe by exactly the right amount
- b increase the length, and therefore the strength, of the bolts
- c allow no pressure to pass the flange
- d allow a reduced pressure of flow along the pipe

Fig. 8.4

5 The insertion of blank flanges, locking-off valves, and placing of warning notices, are all practices used
- a when dismantling drains containing water
- b before dismantling systems at pressure or containing flammable contents
- c for welding up pipework on water towers
- d when assembling pipework systems

6 Refer to Fig. 8.5 in order to answer questions 6-9.
The number of signatures required on the 'Permit to Work' before starting to work on the refrigeration plant would be:
a 5
b 2
c 6
d 4

---

7 These signatures are required to ensure that:
a the electrical supplies are isolated
b the refrigeration system is gas-free and the cold storage facility is available
c the refrigeration system has been isolated
d the work instructions have been understood and all safety precautions are complete and certified

---

8 On completion of the work the permit is signed by the:
a electrical engineer
b worker who repaired the plant
c refrigeration room foreman
d factory inspector

---

9 The colour bands on pipes are an aid to identifying:
a any combination of b, c and d
b system contents
c system pressures
d system temperatures

A Permit-to-Work authorising the performance of maintenance work on a refrigeration plant might include:

(1) Period of validity from ________ hrs to ________ hrs on ________

(2) Issuing authority ________

(3) Identification of plant to be worked on ________

(4) Description of work ________

(5) Safety action to be taken:

(a) Electrical supplies isolated Signature ________

(b) Cold storage permission Signature ________

(c) Refrigeration system isolated Signature ________

(d) Refrigeration system 'gas freed' Signature ________

(6) Acceptance
I certify that I understand the above instructions and that this permit is valid unless all safety actions have been completed and certified.

Time ________ Date ________ Signature ________

(7) Completion of work
I certify that the work for which this permit was issued has been completed and that the equipment is fit for return to service.

Time ________ Date ________ Signature ________

Fig. 8.5

---

10 The removal and replacement of fuses for electrically powered machines must be carried out by:
a the foreman in charge of the machines
b a safety officer
c a person trained to work on live electrical circuits
d a fitter carrying out the repair

---

11 The 'locking-off' of machines (Fig. 8.6) is done so that:
a the electrical supply cannot be switched on whilst the machine is being repaired
b only competent persons can work the machine
c the machine can be used only in shift time and therefore become more efficient to use
d vital safety devices on the machine cannot be removed

Fig. 8.6

---

12 The procedures to which there must be strict adherence when carrying out work on installations featuring dangerous chemicals are:
a 'Permit to Work' procedures
b all or any necessary combination of a, c and d
c 'locking-off' procedures
d emptying and 'purging' procedures

---

13 Standard procedures as laid down by the organisations operating installations featuring dangerous chemicals can be over-ridden by:
a the maintenance foreman
b a 'Permit to Work'
c a revised maintenance schedule
d statute or the Government Inspectorate

---

14 Light, radioactivity, microwaves and X-rays are all potential sources of:
a harmful radiation
b biological damage
c damage to the eardrums
d toxic material

---

15 A suitable dense shielding that will give a degree of protection against X-rays is made from:

a steel
b iron
c lead
d brass

---

16 State the precautions necessary when assembling and dismantling, to counteract any dangers from:
a pressure or flammability of the contents of the system or components
b electricity

---

17 Fig. 8.7 shows the slinging arrangement for lifting a machine.
a Explain why the slings have been so positioned and what could occur if
 i the saddle was moved
 ii the slings were differently placed
 iii the machine was bumped down on to the floor
b Label the parts on the diagram to show which, when lifting occurs, have to withstand the following forces:
 i tension
 ii bending and shear
c Give reasons why petrol or paraffin must not be used when cleaning off the rust preventatives used to coat bright surfaces during transit

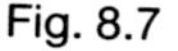

Fig. 8.7

---

9 The effect of material properties

The following questions relate to the above subject. Answers should be given as explained on page 75.

Refer to Fig. 9.1 to answer questions 1-3.

1 Tensile strength is a very important consideration when selecting bolt materials. The material showing the highest tensile strength has a strength of:
a 880 N/mm²
b 780 N/mm²
c 660 N/mm²
d 590 N/mm²

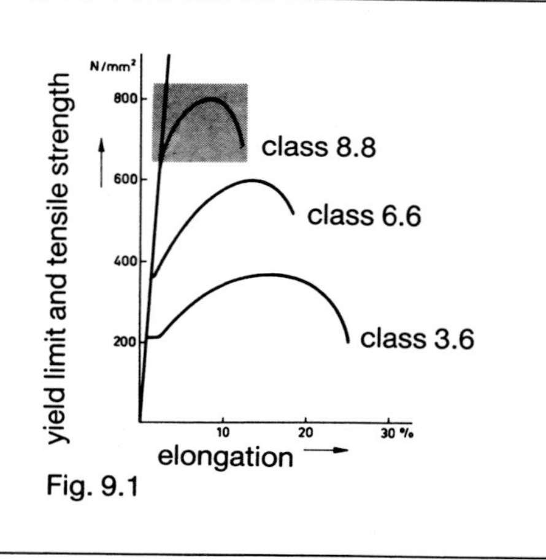

Fig. 9.1

---

2 The elongation % shown on the graph gives an indication of how much, before fracture, the material will:
a compress
b twist
c stretch
d stress

---

3 The yield point or elastic limit is the top of the sloping straight line for each material before the line starts to curve, indicating permanent stretching of the material before fracture. The yield point for a class 6.6 bolt material occurs at:

a 660 N/mm²
b 590 N/mm²
c 360 N/mm²
d 210 N/mm²

4 Drop forged bolts with rolled threads are stronger than machined bolts made from the same material because they:

a are less likely to shear across the threads
b have cap heads
c will accept stronger nuts
d are self-lubricating

---

5 Special materials, such as high tensile steels, are sometimes used for components such as bolts, shafts, etc. These components are identified by:

a the letters H.T.S.
b their colour
c the number of threads
d special markings

---

6 The legs of a pulley drawer have to be strong in:

a tension
b shear
c compression
d twist

---

7 An example of a material strong in tension and shear is

a cast iron
b steel
c plastic
d aluminium

---

8 Materials such as cast iron or hardened steel should not be struck directly with a hammer because:

a the hammer may break
b the component may splinter, causing a safety hazard
c deformation of the material will render it useless
d the face of the hammer is softer than the material and so distorts

---

9 The type of material chosen for pipe seals and packings is dependent upon the nature of the matter flowing through the pipe, the temperature of the matter and the:

a amount it will stretch
b cost of material
c density of the matter flowing through the pipe
d pressure in the pipe

---

10 A material suitable for using as packing where high temperatures are present is:

a corrugated brass
b cork
c rubber
d fibre

---

11 A material suitable for a flange packing on a water pipe is:

a asbestos
b copper
c brass
d compound synthetic rubber

---

12 Which one of the following materials requires more protection from corrosion?

a steel
b aluminium
c copper
d brass

---

13 The surfaces of metals that are likely to corrode in damp atmospheres can be protected by the application of oil, grease, paint, copper, zinc, plastic and:

a steel
b tin
c iron
d hemp

---

14 Zinc-coated steel is known as:

a sheradised steel
b teflon-coated steel
c galvanised steel
d oxidised steel

---

15 Complete the blank spaces in the following chart describing the effects of the properties of materials on assembly and dismantling procedures:

Component	Material	Property and effect of property on assembly/dismantling procedures
Bolt-shank	Mild steel	Good ...., so that the joint will hold and the bolt will not break under tension.
Bolt thread	Mild steel	Good .... so that the threads will not strip.
Key	....	....
Pin punch	High carbon steel	Good toughness, so that the punch will not .... or bend when being hit.
Ball bearing	Hard steel	Good surface h ...., could b .... if force is not applied correctly or material used as drifts is not .... than the bearing material.
Flange packing	Cork	Good .... resistance and can be compressed to shape so that a .... seal can be achieved.

10 General rules

The following questions relate to the above subject. Answers should be given as explained on page 75.

1 The functioning of an assembly must be fully understood:

a before the drawings and specifications are studied
b to assist with assembly and to enable correct operation to be checked on completion of assembly
c to assist the fitter with his selection of tools
d after the assembly has been completed so that testing can be done

2 Before assembly, the correct materials, locking devices, etc. of an assembly should be checked by reference to the:

a relevant British Standard
b information sheet
c assembly drawings and specifications
d assembly operation sequence sheets

3 For all assemblies, the most efficient method of assembly should be worked out before assembly begins. The most likely result of failing to pre-plan a method would be that:

a most of the parts would have to be scrapped
b the parts would have to be removed and re-fitted in another sequence
c the assembly would not function properly on completion
d the assembly would take longer to complete

4 On a new assembly, a valve seat is found to be letting in fluid and so causing malfunction of the assembly. This fault is most likely to be the direct result of:

a not pre-planning the method of assembly
b using the wrong type of valve
c failure to keep dirt etc. out of the valve before and during assembly
d not using the correct materials for valve construction

5 Refer to Fig. 10.1 to answer questions 5-7.
The bolts are tightened in this sequence because:
- a distortion on the workpiece due to tightening is kept to a minimum
- b bolt distortion is kept to a minimum
- c re-setting and adjustments to the wrench are not required
- d this ensures that the torque on the cylinder head bolts is constant

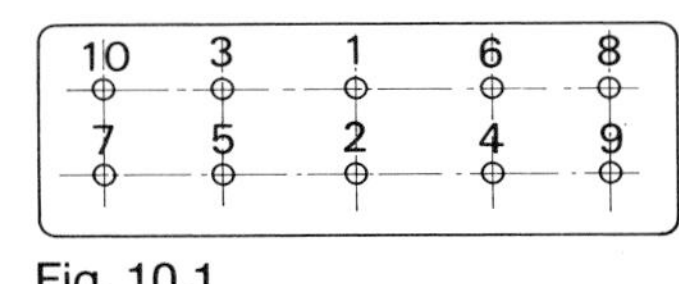

Fig. 10.1

---

6 All bolts are tightened to the same torque so that:
- a the strength of the bolt is maintained during service
- b even tightness of the cylinder head is maintained consistently along its length at all temperatures
- c bolt diameters are constant and not effected by operating temperatures
- d locking devices are not required

---

7 Uneven torque on the bolt heads would most likely result in:
- a breakage of the torque spanner
- b distortion of the cylinder head
- c spring washers having to be fitted under the heads
- d locknuts being used to compensate for any expansion differences

---

Refer to Fig. 10.2 to answer questions 8-11.

8 The correct gap, in what ultimately will be the assembled position of the piston ring is being measured with:
- a a feeler gauge
- b slip gauges
- c shims
- d a knife gauge

a

---

9 The results of the measurements will confirm whether, on assembly, the piston ring gaps will be:
- a set in the correct position to the centre line 'A'
- b in the correct piston recess
- c the correct way up
- d within the specified tolerance

---

10 On assembly, the piston rings that have the gaps set on line 'A' will be:
- a 1 and 2
- b 4 and 3
- c 1 and 4
- d 5 and 2

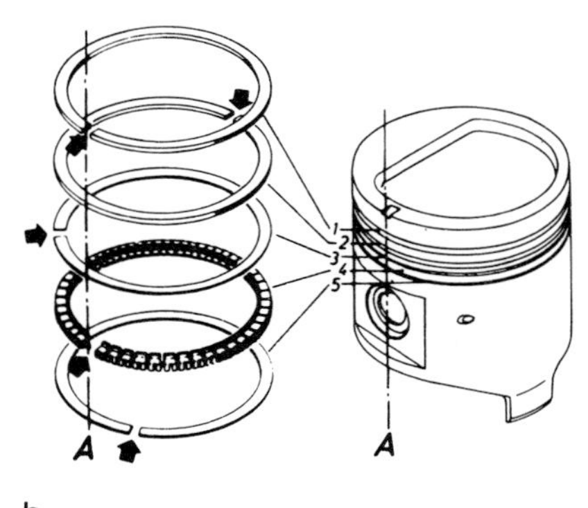

b

Fig. 10.2

---

11 The gaps are arranged in this pre-set position because:
- a it has proved to be the most effective with regard to piston/cylinder sealing
- b they are easier to assemble this way
- c measurement of the gaps is more complex in any other position
- d alignment with the number system is easier than in any other position

12 Refer to Fig. 10.3 to answer questions 12-14.
In relation to the datum line, the setting marks on the table are marked around the circumference every:
a 270°
b 90°
c 360°
d 180°

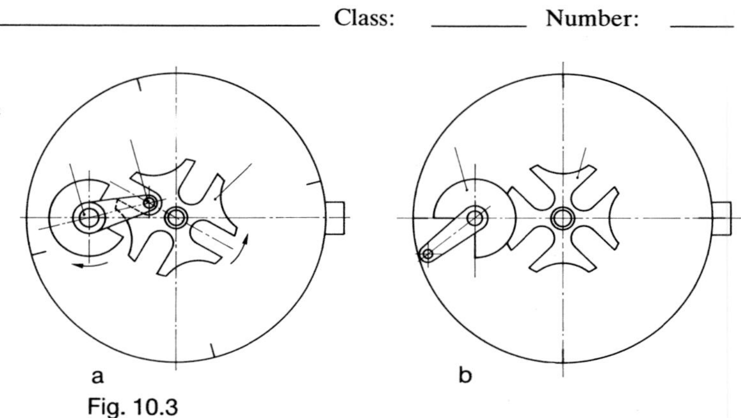

Fig. 10.3

13 When the table and datum mark coincide, the exact angle to the datum of the Geneva Wheel slot will be:
a 90°
b 360°
c 45°
d 180°

14 The best way to prevent axial or radial movement of the Geneva Wheel relative to the table is to:
a tap the end of the shaft and use a stud and locknuts
b key the wheel to the same keyway using a taper key
c tap the end of the shaft and use a set-screw and spring washer
d key the wheel to the same keyway using a feather key

15 Fig. 10.4a shows a power drilling attachment fixed to the slides of a centre lathe. By referring to the exploded view (Fig. 10.4b) complete the following assembling plan for the assembly.

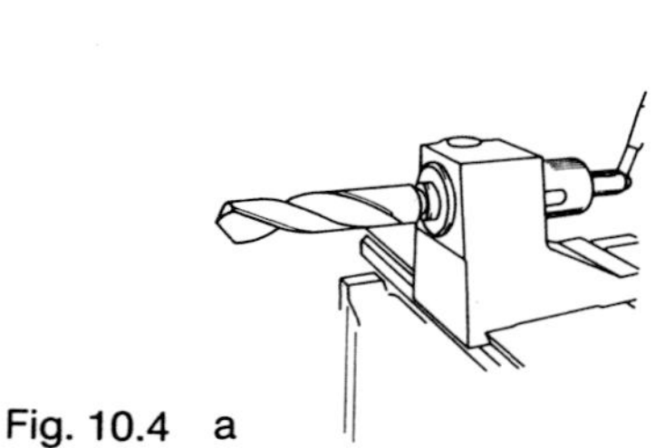

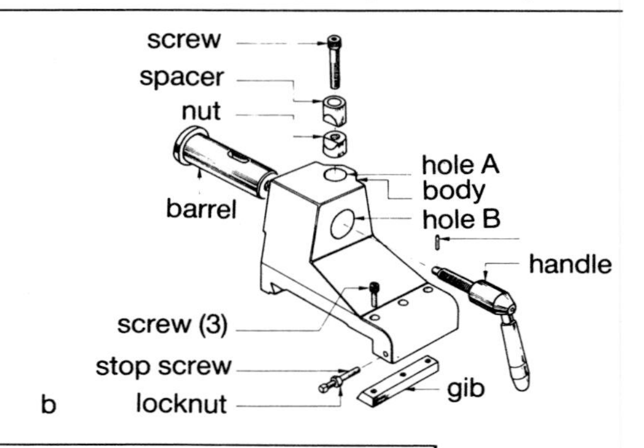

Fig. 10.4 a b

OPERATION DESCRIPTION	TOOLS & EQUIPMENT	SAFETY
1 Fit body to cross slide by tightening gib piece in position	hexagon socket spanner	
2 Position clamp nut in bottom of hole 'A'		
3 .... in hole 'B'		
4 Assemble clamp spacer and screw	....	
5 Screw in .... to barrel		
6	hammer, pin punch	
7		

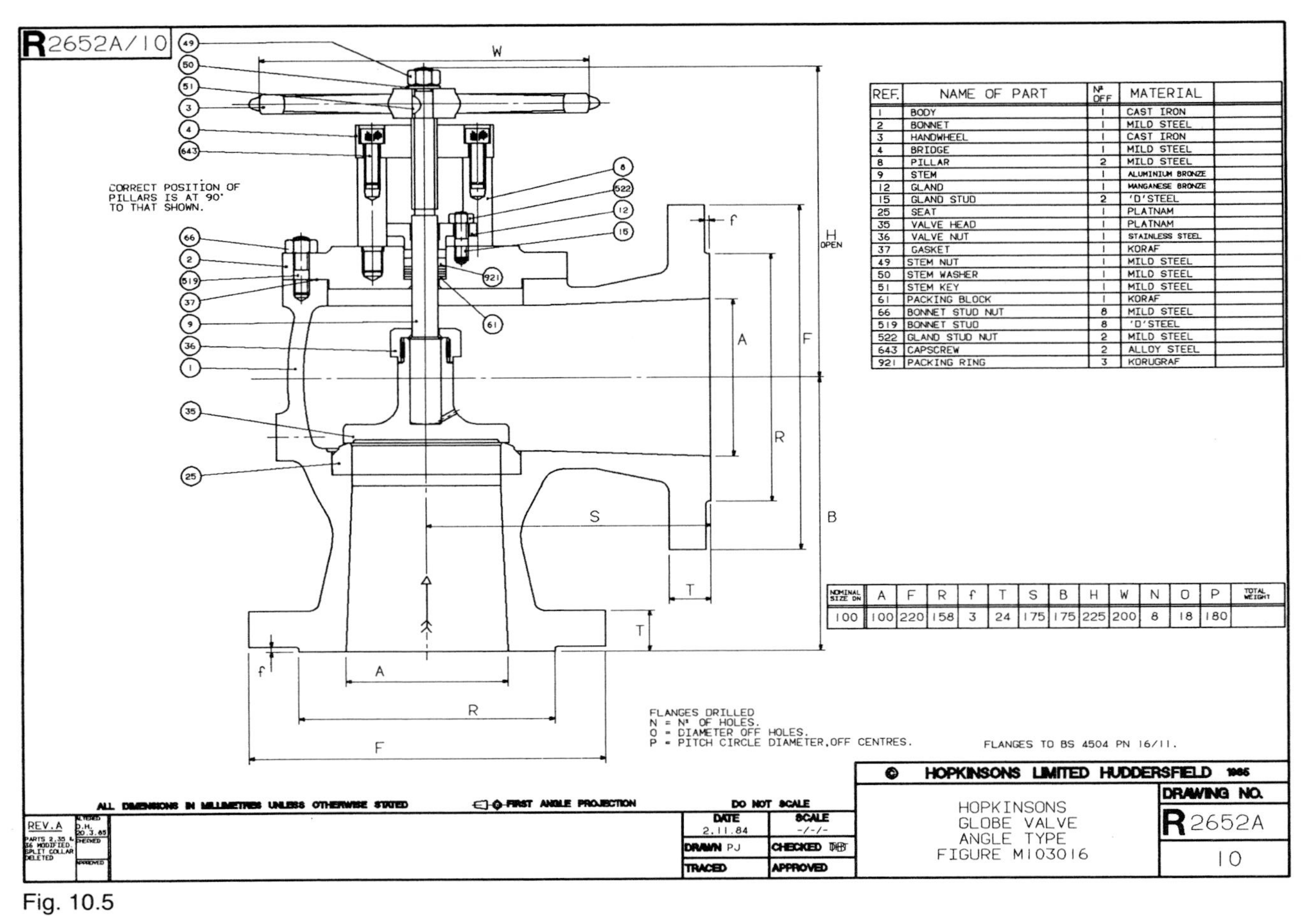

Fig. 10.5

16 Complete the following planning sheet for the strip down of the valve shown at Fig. 10.5, assuming it has been taken out of service and is in the workshop.

OPERATION DESCRIPTION	TOOLS & EQUIPMENT	SAFETY
1 Unscrew stem nut	Open ended spanner	
2	Pulley drawer, Release oil	
3 Dismantle stem key	Drift, hammer, Release oil	
4	Hexagon socket key	
5	.... Extractor	
6 Dismantle gland assembly	Open ended spanner	
7	Open ended spanner, Pry bar	
8 Dismantle valve head	Soft jaw vice	

 Name: ______________________ Class: ________ Number: _____

17 With reference to the valve featured in question 10.16, all parts of the assembly must now be *cleaned and inspected* and, if need be, repaired or replaced before reassembly. Using the following examples as a guide, make out an inspection certificate, in list form for the parts prior to assembly of the valve (Fig. 10.5).

REF	NAME OF PART	No. OFF	MATERIAL	INSPECTION	REPAIR/REPLACE
1	Body	1	Cast iron	Inspect surface for cracks, corrosion	
2	Bonnet	1	Mild steel	Inspect joint surface for residue, packing material and surface damage	
3					
4					
8	Pillar	2		Inspect threads for damage	
9					
12					
15					
etc. to					
921	Packing ring	3			

11 Pipework systems

The following questions relate to the above subject. Answers should be given as explained on page 75.

1 Steel pipes used to convey low to medium pressures are usually:
- a seamed
- b seamless
- c zinc-coated
- d reinforced

2 High pressures are usually accommodated by the use of:
- a zinc-coated pipe
- b seamed tube
- c seamless tube
- d plastic pipe

3 The pipe described in question 1 would be used for:
- a high pressure steam lines
- b hydraulic power pressure lines
- c flexible hydraulic lines
- d gas lines

4 The pipe described in question 2 would be used for:
- a hydraulic pressure lines
- b gas lines
- c water lines
- d drains

5 Precise limits for working pressures used on seamed pipes are not laid down because:
- a the pipe thickness varies considerably along its length
- b they are only 3 mm thick
- c the pipe material varies considerably from one batch to another
- d the joints used are affected by size, service and support conditions and by jointing techniques

6 A pipe material suitable for carrying acids is:
- a steel
- b plastic
- c copper
- d rubber

Table 11.1 Seamless tube materials, sizes, uses and pressures

Material	Diameter mm	Pressure bar	Uses
Steel	6-42	633-151	High pressure fluids such as hydraulic oil and high pressure steam.
Cast iron	80-300 300-1600	40 25	Low pressure fluids such as gas, water or oil drainage lines, although it is used for steam and water main lines at higher pressures.
Copper (soft)	4-12	128-64	Medium pressure fluids such as compressed air, hydraulic oil, and water.
Copper (½ hard)	4-28	340-90	As above but higher pressures may be used.
Plastics	4-28	26-15	Widely used on small diameter pneumatic, low pressure hydraulic and water systems.
Plastics	28 plus		Large capacity feed and drain systems such as cooling lines.

Use the above table only as a guide.

Refer to Table 11.1 to answer questions 7-9.

7 The material that can take the greatest pressure is:
a plastic
b steel
c cast iron
d copper

---

8 A copper (½ hard) pipe ∅ 28 mm will take an approximate pressure of:
a 340 bar
b 60 bar
c 90 bar
d 128 bar

---

9 A gas line is to work at 25 bar and is ∅ 600 mm. A suitable material for this line would be:
a steel
b copper
c plastic
d cast iron

Questions 10 and 11 are related.

10 When consecutive lengths of pipe are directly connected in a run, the assembly is termed:
a 'in length'
b 'in line'
c a connection length
d 'adjacent line'

---

11 A typical joint for such an assembly is:
a a welded joint
b a flange joint
c a screwed joint
d a, b or c

---

12 A 'cross flange' or 'tee piece' is a type of pipe joining device used to make:
a 'in line' connections
b straight connections
c angle connections
d branch connections

---

13 Refer to Fig. 11.1 to answer this question. A socket connector is used to join two pipes. The socket or 'female' thread is usually parallel and the pipe or 'male' thread is:
a tapered
b metric
c parallel
d axial

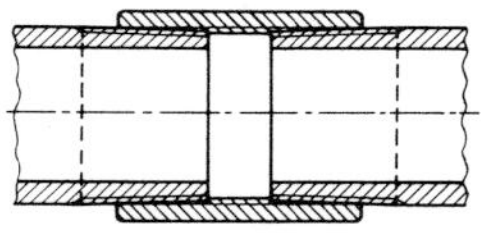

Fig. 11.1

---

14 Sleeved joints on plastic pipes are best sealed by using:
a hemp
b lead and hemp
c rubber or an adhesive
d cork

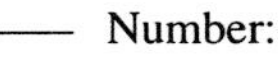

15 Refer to Fig. 11.2 to answer this question. The sleeved joints shown can be used for gas and liquids on large iron pipes and:

a the pipes must be exactly in line but will accommodate expansion
b will allow expansion and slight angular misalignments
c will allow only slight angular misalignments
d will allow axial movements of the two pipes

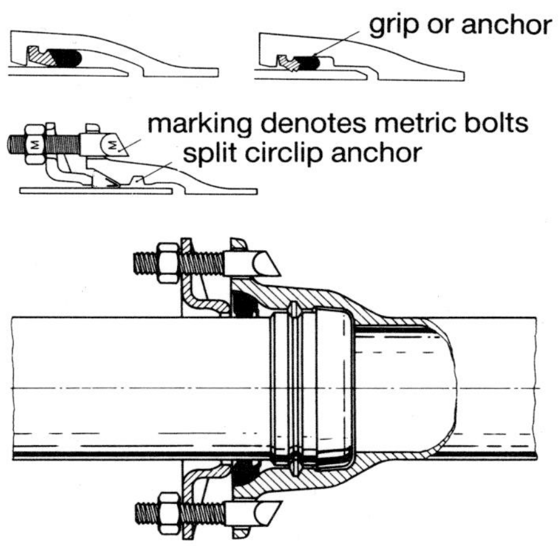

grip or anchor
marking denotes metric bolts
split circlip anchor

Fig. 11.2

Refer to Figs. 11.3/11.4 to answer questions 16-18.

16 The type of fitting that makes use of the principle of squeezing a sleeve on to a pipe to provide a seal is known as a:

a taper fitting
b compression fitting
c ring fitting
d cone fitting

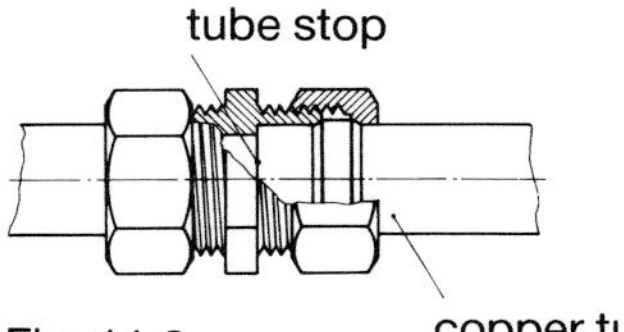

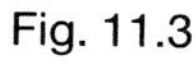

Fig. 11.3

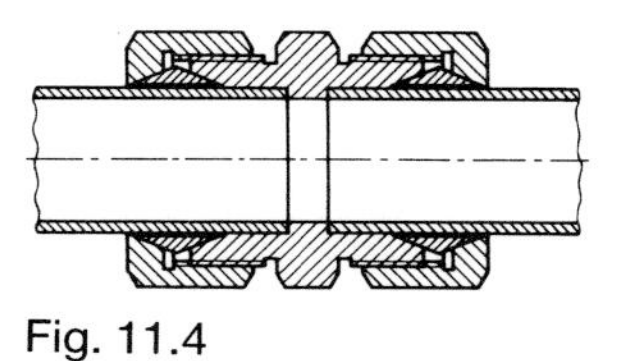

Fig. 11.4

Questions 17-9 refer to the type of fitting discussed in question 16.

17 This type of fitting can be used effectively on:

a a water system
b a hydraulic system
c a pneumatic system
d either systems a, b or c

Questions 18 and 19 are related.

18 This type of fitting must never be used on a:

a pneumatic system
b hydraulic system
c water system
d gas system

---

19 The fitting described in question 16 should not be used on the system selected as the answer to question 18 because:

a possible leaks at the joint become a major safety hazard
b they are not capable of high pressure sealing
c they are not capable of low pressure sealing
d they are not capable of expansion

20 In Fig. 11.5 the taper joint can be sealed using:
a teflon tape
b a captive rubber seal
c a copper washer
d a bonded seal

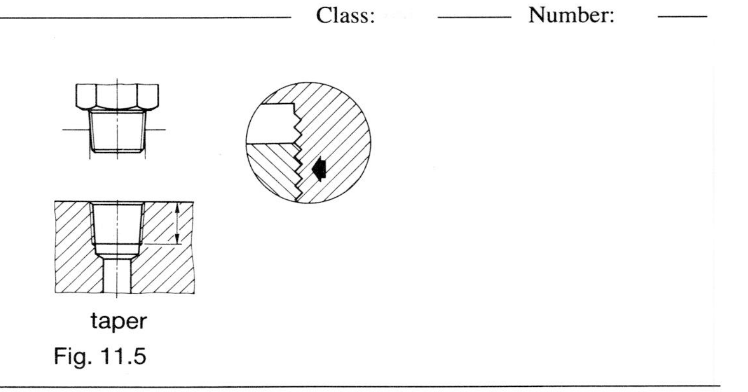

Fig. 11.5

Refer to Fig. 11.6 to answer questions 21 and 22.

21 A typical application for the low pressure fitting would be connecting:

a a hydraulic pump to a lathe copying attachment
b a hydraulic press to a pump
c a high pressure air line to a machine
d a coolant pump to a moving lathe slide

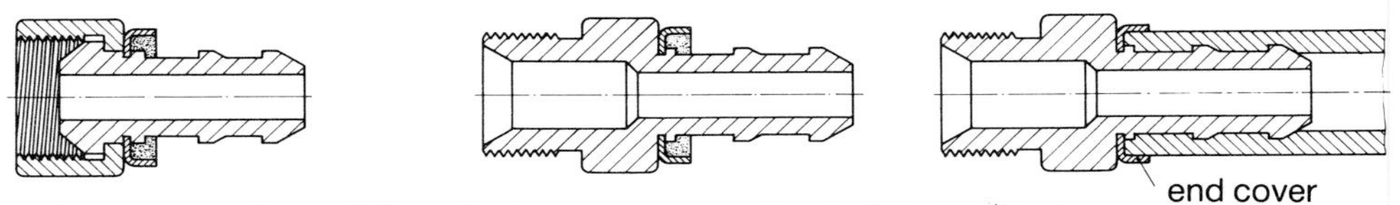

a low pressure hose: fittings for low pressure work only fit inside the hose

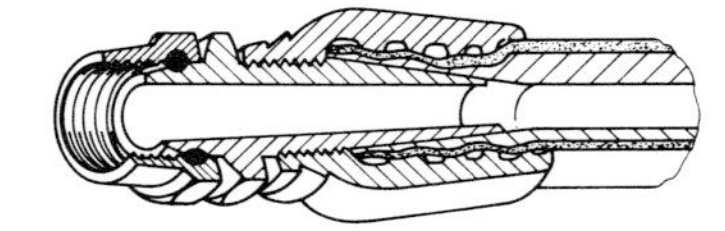
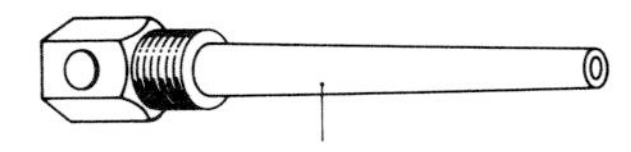

b medium pressure hose: fittings for medium pressure work fit both inside and outside the hose

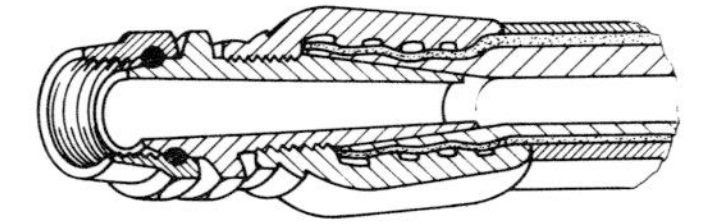

c high pressure hose:
fittings for high pressure work fit inside the hose and around the metal reinforcement of the hose

Fig. 11.6

22 A typical application for the high pressure fitting would be connecting:

a a water pump to a compressor
b a coolant pump to a lathe slide
c a hydraulic cylinder to a pump
d spray to a fire hose

23 Hemp and sealing compound is used to seal:

a hydraulic fittings
b parallel screwed joints
c compression fittings
d expansion joints

24 Sealing tape can be used to seal:

a flange faces
b both parallel and taper screw fittings
c parallel screw fittings only
d taper screw fittings only

25 The sealing of a compression joint requires:

a a sleeve being pressed on to the pipe
b a sealing compound
c hemp and sealing compound
d a sleeve being expanded on to the nuts and pipe

26 A compression joint suitable for use on a hydraulic system using steel tubes would have olives made from:

a brass
b PTFE
c alloy steel
d mild steel

27 The olives would be made from the material identified in question 11.26 so that they would:

a be hard enough to bite into the pipe
b be rustproof and soft
c compress on to the pipe and mould to it
d be cheap enough to throw away when remaking the joint

28 Where strength and sealing of the joint is of the utmost importance a flange is best attached to a pipe by:

a welding
b screw threads and sealing compound
c brazing
d soldering

29 The type of process relying on capillary action to join a flange to a pipe is:

a bronze welding
b welding
c brazing
d fusion welding

30 Brass, steel and plastic flanges can all be joined to pipes by:

a bronze welding
b brazing
c soldering
d welding

31 Flanges are sealed by using:

a PTFE tape
b packings
c hemp and sealing compound
d sealing compound

32 The type of sealing device used for flange sealing is influenced by:

a pipe contents
b temperature
c pipe material
d a combination of a, b and c

33 Leakage at flange joint faces will occur if the:

a flange holes are 45° to the horizontal
b pipe thread is tight
c faces are not parallel with each other
d faces are not covered with jointing compound

34 A flange joint is found to be leaking after tightening the flange bolts in random order. It is leaking because the:

a packing has been distorted
b sealing compound has been squeezed out
c bolts have stretched
d holes are out of alignment

35 Expansion of a pipe is expected most when it is:

a in a vertical position
b carrying hot materials
c in a horizontal position
d ready for service checks

36 Failure to include expansion joints in the situation referred to in question 35 will result in:

a no expansion of the pipes
b only expansion along the length of the pipe
c more load being put on the connected equipment
d loss of strength of the pipe material

37 When there is a considerable movement of pipes owing to expansion, rollers are used to:

a make radial expansion easier
b stop heat losses
c regulate temperatures
d make axial movement easier

38 The type of equipment used to check that the face of a flange is parallel to the centre line or axis of a pipe is:

a a dial test indicator
b an engineer's rule
c a tri-square
d an engineer's rule and tri-square

39 Three pipe lengths are joined 'in line', with the centre length having an equal sized 'branch line' connection. Make a sketch to indicate the type of fitting used, the 'in line' connections, and the 'branch' connection.

---

40 a Complete the following table on the types of pipe used on the press illustrated in Figs. 11.7 and 11.8.

	PIPE		USE/COMMENT
	Material	Type	
1	Steel	....	Used on high hydraulic pressure side system
2	....	Seamed	Used on low return pressure side of system
3	....	Seamless	Small bore, easily to bent shape and flared

b Refer to Fig. 11.8. What are the types of fittings used on the high pressure hydraulic tube? Describe how sealing is achieved.

____

____

____

____

c Refer to Fig. 11.8. What are the types of fittings used on the low pressure pipes? Describe how sealing is achieved.

____

____

____

____

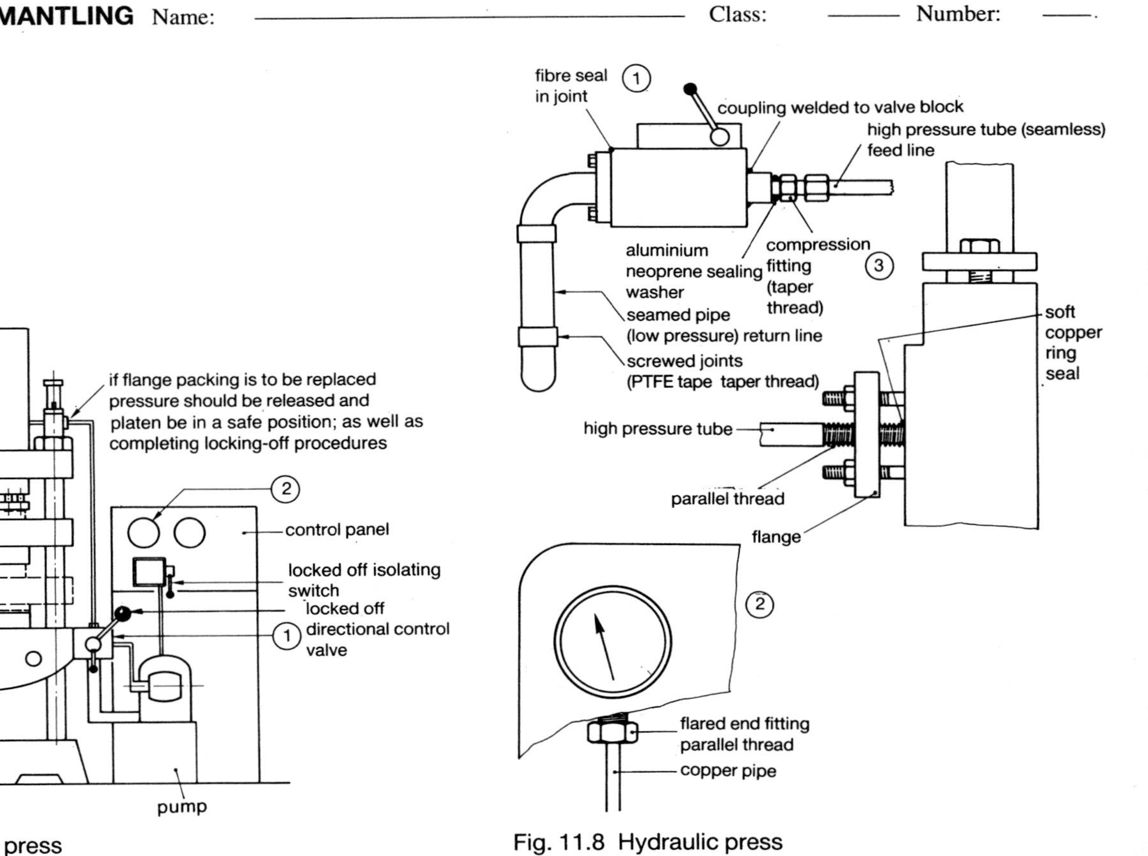

Fig. 11.7 Hydraulic press

Fig. 11.8 Hydraulic press

41 Complete the following table of sealing materials and uses.

Sealing material		Used to seal
Cork		....
Compounds		oil water
Paper/greased or varnished		water oil etc
PTFE		....
Rubber/natural and synthetic		water oil chemicals etc
Graphite impregnated cloth		....
Metals:	aluminium copper steel berylium copper/corrugated brass	high pressure high temperature gases and liquids

12 Dismanting pipework

The following questions relate to the above subject. Answers should be given as explained on page 75.

1 If a pipe is found to be in a corroded state, it should be dismantled safely and replaced because it could:
- a fracture and cause a loss of the contents
- b fracture and the contents cause serious accidents
- c contaminate the pipe contents
- d cause a combination of a, b and c

2 Modification of a system layout, repair of a valve, or unblocking a clogged pipe may all be described as:
- a repair jobs on pipework systems
- b possible reasons for dismantling a pipework system
- c jobs done in the workshop
- d carefully executed, pre-planned fault rectification on pipework systems

3 Dismantling and repairing of pipework systems is usually carried out in shutdown time and must be:
- a kept to a minimum time
- b undertaken at night
- c done in teabreaks and lunchtimes
- d undertaken by the safety officer and a pipe fitter

4 When planning a shutdown of a pipework system, action must be taken to make pipes:
- a pressure-free
- b dry
- c pressure-free and shut off
- d aerated, with a constant flow of dry air

5 When dismantling a pipework system carrying liquids or gases which could be dangerous to health; before work commences the system must be:
- a drained
- b drained and purged
- c exhausted
- d covered with a safety tent

6 On a pipework circulation system containing water, a pipe has to be drained of liquid in order to facilitate repair. The drain point should be:
- a at the lowest point of the pipework
- b next to a valve
- c at the highest point of the pipework
- d on the pipework centre point

Refer to Figs. 11.7 and 11.8 to answer questions 7-11.

7 When pressurised, the jack rams hold the platen in the top or open position; if pressure is released the platen will:
- a stay in a neutral position
- b stick in the open position
- c stay in the open position
- d drop to the closed position

8 Before work can be started safely on dismantling pipework of the press:
- a both b and d must be completed and then 'locked off'
- b the isolation switch must be put in the *off* position
- c all the pipe joints must be tightened to prevent leakage
- d the directional control valve must be operated to release pressure

9 The most appropriate special purpose tool for dismantling the pipe connecting the pressure gauge would be:
- a an adjustable 'C' hook spanner
- b a box spanner
- c a pipe nut spanner
- d an extra deep socket

---

10 The high pressure tube feed line should be dismantled by:
- a unscrewing the taper thread from the socket
- b sawing off the socket
- c unscrewing the nut to release the compression ring
- d sawing through the feed line

---

11 To renew a screwed joint in the middle of a complex screwed pipe system, the best method of dismantling would be to:
- a unscrew half the system only
- b cut the adjacent pipe
- c put in a bypass line
- d unscrew the joint only

---

12 Refer to Fig. 12.1. To allow withdrawal, if 1 is equal to 2.5 mm the minimum movement of the adjacent pipework is:
- a 2.5 mm
- b 5 mm
- c 0
- d 25 mm

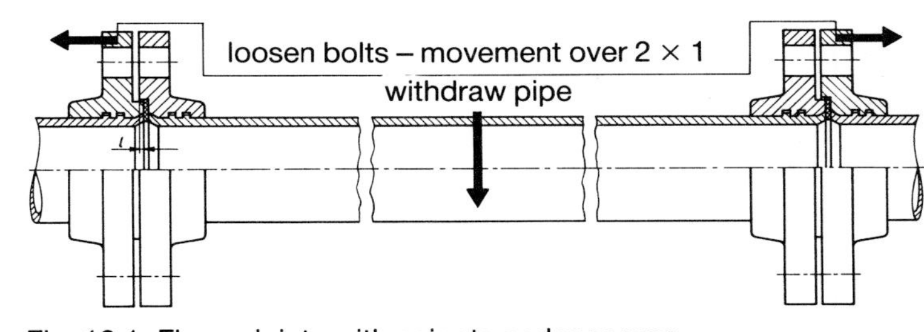

Fig. 12.1 Flange joints with spigots and recesses

---

13 Failure to remove old packings completely from flange faces before renewing them during assembly can lead to:
- a incorrect materials being used
- b stressing of the flange bolts
- c expansion rates increasing
- d leakage at the flange face

---

14 On inspection a set of flange bolts and nuts is found to have rounded corners. These must be replaced in the flange assembly because they:
- a could be responsible for dangerous leaks at the flange faces
- b may wear the threads down and so affect bolt strength
- c cannot be tightened
- d may cause damage to the spanner faces

---

15 When replacing flange bolts, care should be taken to ensure that they are:
- a of mild steel, to British Standard quality
- b checked for suitability and specification
- c hexagon headed S.I. bolts
- d of high tensile steel

---

16 Fill in the blank spaces to complete the following table on the safe emptying of a petrol pipe system prior to the system being dismantled.

OPERATIONS 1 and 2	1 DRAINING LIQUIDS	2 RECOVERING GASES
Observation of safety rules	Bond correctly ....hose Display hazard signs in the appropriate place	.... hose Display ....
Making connections	Connect drain hose to special .... and .... point of system	Connect drain hose to .... point in system and safe discharge point
Venting	....	Open air inlet most .... pump
Pumping or draining	.... the liquid out of pipe work. close and disconnect drain line.	Pump the vapour to a safe discharge area.

17 Along lines similar to the table in question 16 make up a suitable table for the safe emptying of ammonia pipelines.

ASSEMBLING AND DISMANTLING Name: ______________________ Class: ________ Number: _____

The following questions span the syllabus subject matter and approximate to the level of those in the relevant examination paper of the City and Guilds of London Institute. Answers should be short and clear.

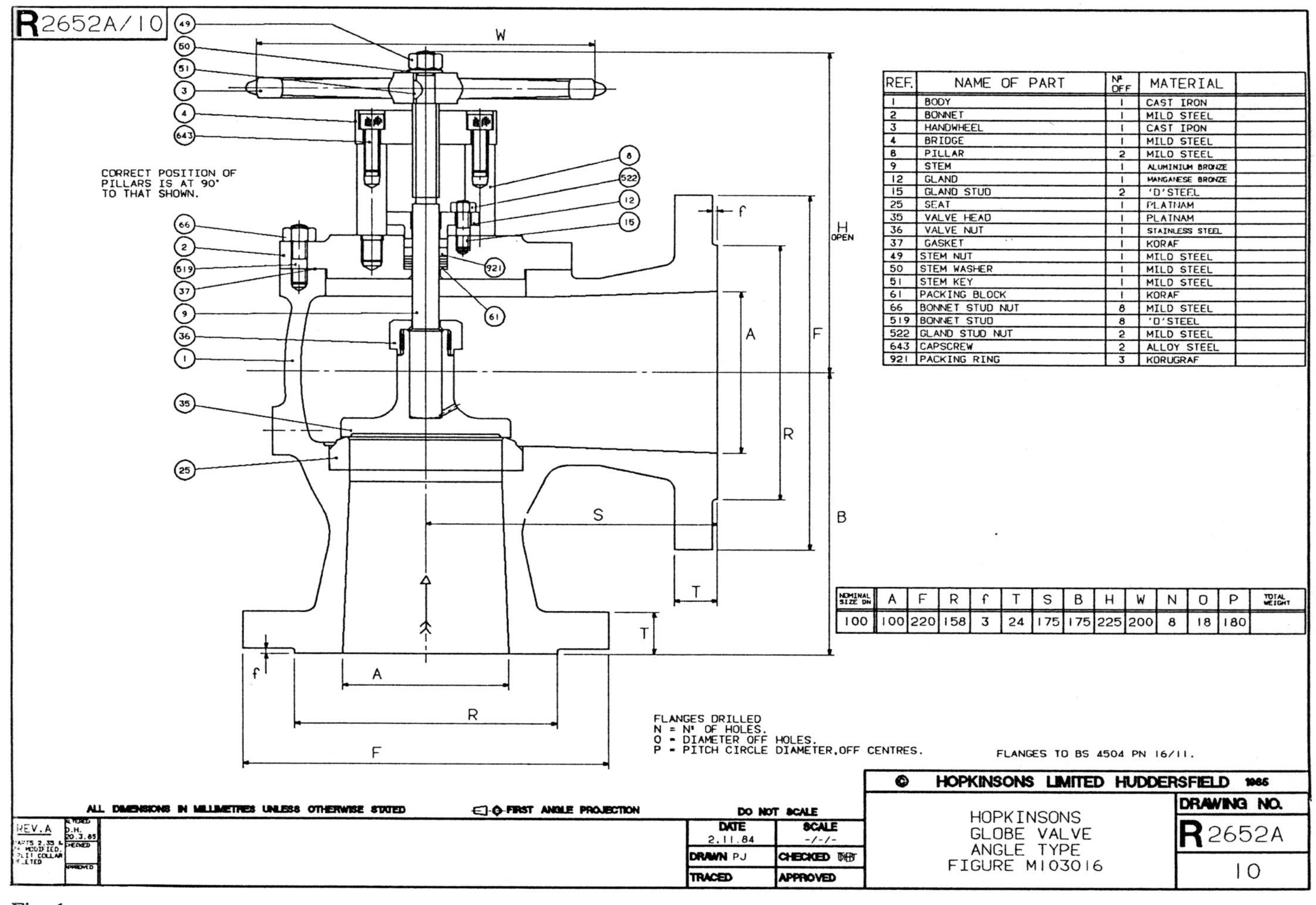

Fig. 1

Refer to Fig. 1 to answer questions 1-3.

1 The type of material used to make the stem is:
- a cast iron
- b mild steel
- c alloy steel
- d aluminium bronze

2 Complete strip down of the valve assembly would start by dismantling part number:
- a 3
- b w
- c 49
- d 50

3 During service it is suspected that the valve seat is worn. On site inspection of the seat can be best achieved by:
- a uncoupling the bonnet stud nuts and taking out the relevant parts
- b dismantling the bridge and removing it
- c uncoupling the horizontal flanges
- d uncoupling the vertical flanges

4 In order to achieve the dismantling required in question 3 quickly, the type of equipment required would be a:
a socket wrench set
b set of hexagon sockets
c set of open-ended spanners
d screw driver and open-ended spanner

---

5 Refer to Fig. 2. An alternative method of preventing damage when dismantling the screw would be to:
a apply some grease to the thread before unscrewing
b file down the end of the component to below the minor diameter of the thread
c apply some release oil to the thread before unscrewing
d heat the end of the component so that it is soft

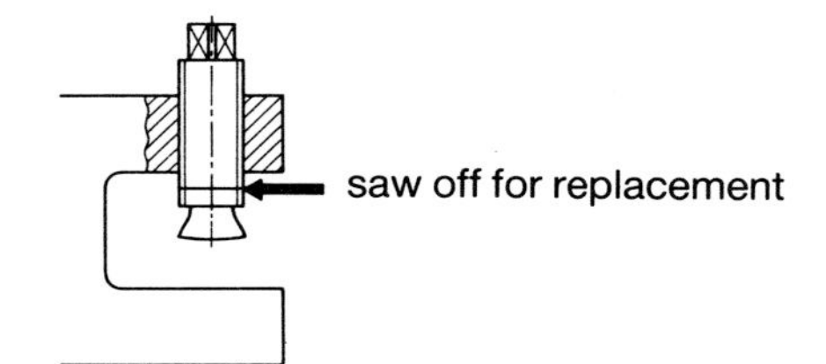

Fig. 2 Preventing damage in dismantling

---

6 Drifts should always be made from softer material than that of the part being dismantled because failure to do so would most likely lead to the:
a drift being bent
b component being damaged
c component sticking
d force transmitted being magnified

---

7 The most suitable material for making a drift to extract a brass bush from a casting would be:
a mild steel
b tool steel
c aluminium alloy
d lead

---

8 Oil is applied to threads, shafts, pulleys, keys and slides when dismantling because it:
a prevents rusting
b makes the force necessary for dismantling greater
c prevents damage from percussion instruments
d makes dismantling easier

---

9 Refer to Fig. 3. A drive shaft runs in bearings similar to those shown. They are numbered in a similar manner, 1 to 6. This is done because:
a there are six bearings
b on re-assembly this helps identify both place and position of each bearing
c this corresponds to the drawing specification number
d on dismantling this gives the sequence of unfastening

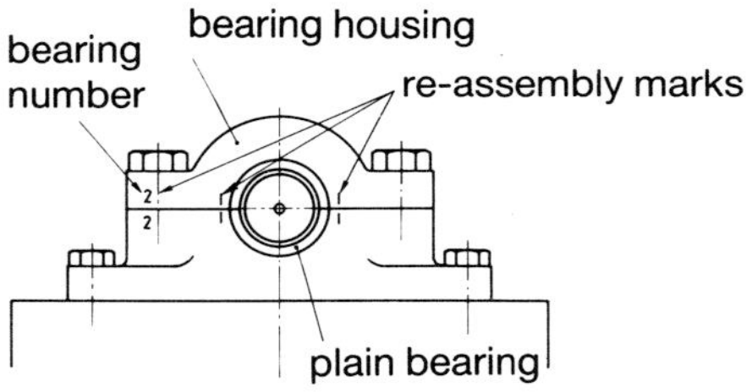

Fig. 3 Position and relationship marks

Questions 10 and 11 are related.

10 On inspection of the oil in a machine gear box, dirt and metallic contamination was found. The contamination was most probably due to:
a inadequately filtering the oil
b excessive wear on gears, bearings and seals
c running the machine for long periods of time
d running the machine at fast speeds

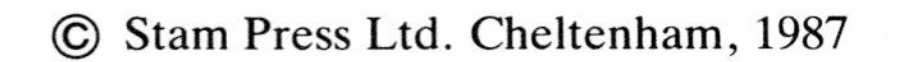

11 The most likely result of the condition referred to in question 10 would be:
- a excessive play on gears and bearings
- b tightness of the bearings
- c no play between the gears
- d no clearance on the oil seals

Questions 12 and 13 are related.

12 In the dismantling of assemblies, components are usually cleaned and inspected. To facilitate storage before assembly takes place, the components should be:
- a placed carefully in a refrigerated box
- b held in suspension oil
- c covered with a suitable material
- d removed from site to a central store

---

13 The components are stored as described in question 12 to:
- a prevent dirt getting on them
- b keep them at the correct temperature
- c stop them rusting
- d keep them with all the other parts in the factory

---

14 'Permit to Work', 'locking-off' and 'lifting' all involve safety rules and procedures. Which of the points below best describes the action needed to follow them?
- a looked up before assembling components
- b the workforce being made aware of all safety rules on recruitment and these rules being strictly applied and observed
- c displayed in the fitting shop
- d looked up before dismantling of machines begins